Vets in the Wild

The real stories behind the BBC television series

Steve Leonard and Trude Mostue

BⓍXTREE

First published in 1999 by Boxtree,
an imprint of
Macmillan Publishers Ltd,
25 Eccleston Place, London, SW1W 9NF,
Basingstoke and Oxford.
Associated companies throughout the world.

ISBN 0 7522 1773 9

1 3 5 7 9 8 6 4 2

A CIP catalogue record for this book is available from
the British Library.

Design by Jane Coney
Photographs by Andres Bifani © BBC
Colour reproduction by Speedscan
Printed in Italy by New Interlitho

This book ties in to the BBC/Animal Planet
television series
produced and directed by Michael Massey.

CONTENTS

CHAPTER 1

South Africa

Day one

Trude: So finally I am sitting on the plane on my way to Johannesburg. I've been waiting for a long time for this moment, and now it feels so unreal. I am actually going to Africa! After having worked so hard for the last six months it will be exciting to change my surroundings completely: new country, new culture, new climate, new people and, not least, completely different kinds of animals … It will certainly be different from my hamsters and moody Jack Russell terriers in Staple Hill. The guys I will be dealing with here will be stronger, bigger and have sharper teeth – and more of them! Just the thought of getting the chance to see and touch these fantastic animals makes me want be pathetic and female and cry. As a little girl I always had a secret dream to go to Africa and work with these animals – a dream that is about to come true.

I have just read the schedule, and I can't believe that we are actually going to do all these things: darting elephants, walking with rhino babies, health-checking cheetahs and catching crocodiles. It all sounds too good to be true at the moment, it's like going to a different planet. It does scare me a bit too as, obviously, I haven't had any experience with these animals before. But hey, rectalling an elephant must be similar to rectalling a cow. I will just pretend that they are big cows with very long noses.

Steve: I met up with the rest of the team at the airport: Trude, Michael Massey (the director), Gillian Colyer (the assistant producer), Denis Borrow (the cameraman) and 'Cuddly Dudley' Houlden (the sound-man). The filming equipment was a small mountain of aluminium cases. Trude and I were really hyped up about the trip, and Michael was letting us in on some of the things we are going to be doing – they sound amazing. Working with elephants, lions and crocodiles is going to be unreal. I don't think it will really register until we get out there and do it. There's just a ten-hour flight between me and the most incredible adventure of my life.

Day Two

Steve: I got very little sleep last night. Plane seats are not designed for my gangly frame. If airlines were subjected to the same standards as livestock transport, they would have been taken to court by the RSPCA by now. We touched down in Johannesburg at 8.40 am. Dressed in shorts and sandals (and thankfully a fleece), we left the plane. Our captain wasn't joking when he said it was -1°C outside. The nights can get very cold in winter but the sky was cloudless and the day was a very pleasant 25–30°C. We were met by Andres Bifani (who is both our location manager and the trip's photographer) and his brother Matias. They had the vehicles already waiting for us. Matias was to drive a Toyota Hilux 4x4 pick-up, while Andres was driving a Land Rover Discovery. We will pick up the vetmobile in a few days' time as apparently it hasn't been fully converted yet.

Trude: We had a very long drive from Johannesburg to Kruger National Park today. Along the road we saw the flashing neon lights of the casinos and big mines, which made me think that this was really quite a different Africa from the one I had expected. South Africa is generally more modern than other African countries, though.

Steve: The terrain looked more like Arizona than South Africa. Red dusty scrubland hills bathed in strong evening sun put me in mind of the Marlboro adverts. On the way, we saw the smoke plumes of some bushfires that Andres told us had been burning for days. With no breeze to disperse it, the smoke formed into huge mushroom clouds thousands of metres high. The whole scene was like the start of some apocalyptic science-fiction movie.

Our overnight stop is Karos Kruger Lodge, just outside Kruger National Park. It's like the Ewok village in *Return of the Jedi,* with all the gangways suspended between trees and lit by lanterns. The rooms are really nice, and the bed looks very inviting after last night on the plane and such a long day. At dinner we met JJ van Altena, who works in the park with the Game Capture Team. We discussed tomorrow's filming over a fantastic meal. The temperature had fallen markedly with the setting of the sun, and I could see my breath. Thankfully, there were wood-burning braziers made out of old metal barrels strategically placed around our tables, which kept us warm.

Trude: We met JJ today. He is a nice young man who is going to take us trekking to find elephants tomorrow. I am starting to feel slightly nervous about these big animals, and the thought of being on foot and not in a car seems a bit too brave to me at the moment. It's amazing to meet someone that actually does this for a living. I have thousands of questions to ask – I'm starving for information! Both Steve and I are so excited about every little thing. The hamsters at home are not so scary any more. I am tired after all the travelling though, so will read a bit about elephants and then go to bed.

Day three

Trude: The morning started cold and bright. I had a good night's sleep, only waking up now and then to hear the hyenas in the bush next to the lodge.

Steve: This morning we teamed up early with JJ and his tracker, Paul, and headed out into the park. On the way JJ told me about the elephant contraceptive project. The main problem is elephant overpopulation, which leads to habitat destruction. The control of elephant numbers had been achieved by culling. This is a complicated issue, as the death of one member of a group causes great distress to the remaining elephants. Therefore it was decided to cull entire herds, including the calves – hardly an ideal situation. The contraceptive programme aims to decrease the need to cull while causing minimal distress to the elephants.

Trude: Immuno-contraception is in its experimental stages at the moment but might prove to be a better and more humane method of preventing pregnancies than the other methods that are currently in use. We are going to find out if the big girls are responding to a contraceptive injection, and see if this method of controlling the elephant population is viable and practical.

Steve: The elephants we were tracking had radio collars on, so everyone, including JJ, expected to find them very easily. However, the signal only travels as far as you can see, and the area the elephants were in was huge. We travelled up and down the tracks, stopping every so often and climbing on to the roof of our vehicle to scan the bush with the receiver. After a few hours, JJ picked up a faint signal deep in the most inaccessible part of the park. Undaunted, we headed off along a vague track, but soon it became clear that this wasn't the best place to take the Land Rover. Gillian

Did you know?

Elephants can't jump or gallop, but can reach speeds of 30 kph.

and Trude stayed behind while the crew, JJ and I continued crashing over bushes and rocks in JJ's vehicle. I winced and grimaced as the thorny branches bashed against the windows and scraped all along the paintwork. I suppose you just get used to it.

After a few hours we still had only weak signals from the elephants. However, JJ was convinced we were getting close. Eventually we had to abandon the vehicle because the terrain had got too rough, and JJ thought we were close enough to track on foot. This was welcome news, as I was rapidly nodding off in the front seat. JJ loaded his rifle and strapped a pistol around his waist, which made me realize just how vulnerable we were. With a quick run through the rules – no talking, walk in single file and whistle or click to get each other's attention – we set off. Now my blood was pumping. I was surprised that JJ was so noisy as he walked. He strode ahead, not looking where his feet were, treading on branches and scuffing the ground. I was convinced any animal within a mile of us was going to know we were coming. We walked in a large circle, trying to get downwind of where JJ thought the herd was. The vegetation consisted mainly of ankle-height thorny bushes with the occasional copse of trees, and soon all our ankles were bleeding and raw.

Trude: Gillian and I had to wait in the Land Rover while Steve and the others continued to track the elephants on foot. We waited and waited for them to come back. We were in the middle of the bush with long grass everywhere, and we couldn't get out of the Land Rover as this was lion country. As far as we were concerned, there could be lions and mambas in the grass. We both thought it was wiser to stay in the vehicle. It was a good opportunity for Gillian and I to get to know each other better, so we started to tell each other our life stories, which was very interesting! We had a good laugh over the best and the worst boyfriends we'd had, and at the end of the waiting period we felt we knew each other very well.

Steve: Suddenly we saw about six elephants moving ahead of us in some trees. As we followed them JJ stopped and pointed at what appeared to be two large, grey boulders. One of them suddenly flicked its ear. They were two young male white rhinos – the first rhinos I'd seen in the wild – and they were only 30 metres away. JJ signalled for us to circle them so that we would pass downwind. Adrenalin pumping, I followed JJ, never once taking my eyes off the huge sleeping forms. Michael motioned for us to stop while we filmed the rhinos. As he set up the tripod for the camera it clicked. The rhinos were on their feet and whirling round to face us in under a second. Nobody moved for about a minute as they looked in our general direction, snorting like bulls. JJ whispered to me that although rhinos' eyesight is poor, their hearing and sense of smell are very acute. I now understood why we could crash along as we were walking. These were normal sounds to these rhinos, unlike the click of the tripod.

Trude: Although I had felt a bit annoyed about having been left behind, I now felt lucky that I'd had the opportunity to talk to Gillian, and I had really enjoyed our time together. In between chatting we stared into the bush. It was a very strange experience, as any second a lion might pop up from the grass and surprise us. Most of the animals sleep in the shade or in the long grass in the middle of the day, and it would be very easy to stumble over one. At one stage Gillian just had to go to the toilet behind the Land Rover. I was looking out for lions while we both giggled nervously.

Steve: Leaving the rhino, we moved on until we came upon the most spectacular site I had ever seen: a herd of seventy or eighty elephants, with their young, walking up a river bed. It was so hard to take it all in. They moved slowly and gently around a corner, stopping to feed and drink on the way, and so gave us plenty of time to observe them from the bank. As

▼ Trude and Steve getting to know Douw Grobler – or Mr Growler as he became to Trude – the vet they worked with in South Africa.

we were watching them, Paul whistled softly and pointed into the bush, where three or four elephants were approaching from our flank. JJ decided it was time to leave. We moved a little way off and stopped to film JJ. Suddenly there was an almighty scream from the bushes we had come from. We all froze. One of the elephants had probably picked up our smell and was warning the others. Thankfully, Michael said he had enough footage, and we departed.

Trude: We waited for three and a half hours before we finally got contact from the walkie-talkie. We were both relieved that the boys were OK. Although it had been a bit of a wait, it was lovely to be in the bush.

Steve: Our accommodation in the park is basic but very welcome. There are hot showers and a bed, which is all I really require. Trude, Michael and I spent half an hour doing some keep-fit exercises. Michael challenged me to a skipping contest which I lost, due to my shorts falling down – my excuse, anyway. Michael's new nickname is 'Q', because he has every gadget under the sun with him, including a personal computer and a watch that measures his heart rate – I hope he has enough batteries for the trip!

We arrived late for dinner because Andres got us lost. The park vet, Douw Grobler, was waiting for us and I don't think he was very happy. Douw is imposing both in stature and demeanour, but I think I hit it off OK with him. We talked about our day's encounters with the elephants and rhinos while JJ and Douw enthralled us with their tales of charging elephants and their horror story of having to shoot one. Michael asked JJ if he would shoot a charging rhino. JJ just looked at Douw and said, quite seriously, 'You think of something else.' I got the feeling that rhinos are very sacred. Halfway through the meal we heard gunshots. Douw explained that bull elephants were probably trying to break into people's gardens to eat the plants and trees.

Day four

Steve: Up at 6.00 am again this morning. Walking to the shower room, I was greeted by impala, just outside the fence, grazing away quietly. They moved like ballet dancers through the bushes. I don't think I'll ever get used to this bush life.

Trude: This morning we were taken to the rhino 'boma'. As part of a conservation project, the park breeds white rhinos. They also take in rhinos from areas where they might be in danger from poachers. The rhinos have been poached almost to extinction because of their impressive horns. Most rhinos today are living in protected areas as a desperate attempt to try to save them and optimize their chances of survival.

The boma area was bigger than I expected, with big enclosures made up of thick poles. The sun was shining, although the air was still chilly. I felt really excited about seeing a rhino for the first time in my life; I hadn't even seen a rhino in captivity in England. Strips of sunlight were coming through the poles and blinded us at first when we peeked through. Suddenly an enormous grey body moved towards us, and a giant appeared in the dust. I have never seen such a massive creature move so quickly: it was as if it was dancing around in the enclosure. Its small twinkly eyes were peering out at us from between concrete-grey skin folds. The rhino was very graceful, and could turn scarily fast. Douw told us this animal had only recently been captured, and it wasn't used to people yet, hence the mock charges. It will take some time to calm it down.

Steve: Rhinos have very distinct personalities, and respond differently to capture. Most go off their food at first, and if they don't start eating within twelve days they are released. The youngsters that were to be exported for captive breeding programmes were tame enough for us to touch. The most surprising sensation was grasping the horn, as it wobbled at its base. The horn is really a mass of hair fibres, and isn't bony at all. I couldn't believe that this mass of hair drove poachers to hunt these beautiful creatures nearly to the point of extinction.

Running my hands down the rhino's flanks was like caressing warm rock. Their skin is like armour-plating in its thickness and texture. Rhinos have a smooth area of skin on the inside of their thighs and they loved this being rubbed. It was weird to be rubbing these huge creatures and hearing them make little squeaks of pleasure. One of the young rhinos was particularly tame because it had been treated daily for a skin infection next to its horn. The only thing I could relate this experience to was meeting a hand-reared bull who was as tame as a dog. Both animals could kill you within a second, yet I could stand with them and pet them. In some ways, it made me even more aware of their power and size, which was very humbling.

Did you know?

White rhinos only have one horn whereas black rhinos have two. The horns are made of hair fibres and contain no bone.

Trude: We had only been in Douw's office for five minutes this morning when a call came in. A lion had been found injured in the park and a vet was required. All three of us rushed off in Douw's car. Apparently, you do not usually intervene with wildlife in the bush, but in this case, for research purposes, it was a good opportunity to dart an animal

▲ Steve looking more relaxed than he felt as he prepares to dart for the first time.

that would otherwise be killed by hyenas or would die a slow death. There had been problems before with tuberculosis in lions in the park, and Douw wanted to check for this in the injured lion. The park is massive and we were driving very fast, passing confused-looking tourist cars which are only allowed to drive slowly, about 30 kilometres per hour. Although a lot of the park has tarmac roads, we soon hit some dirty, dusty tracks.

We quickly arrived at the site, where the lion was being kept under observation by some rangers. There were tourist cars gathering as they soon realized that something unusual was about to happen. This can cause a problem for the vet – you don't need a traffic jam when you have to get somewhere as quickly as possible. At the same time, Douw thinks the public should be able to take part in such events, as it is the entry fee they pay when they visit the park that funds their work. If the tourists didn't come to the park, the authorities wouldn't be able to operate it as efficiently as they do.

I was feeling very tense, because Steve was going to dart for the first time in his life. I could see he was nervous as well. The lion didn't seem to be bothered about the car at all, most animals in a safari park are used to vehicles. Lots of people take this to mean that they are totally harmless, and there have been stories of tourists climbing out of their car to get a better picture. That is not a good idea unless you are extremely interested in the dental formulae of lions. Once you are out of the car, you become potential dinner for the predators of the park.

Steve: Douw loaded the dart with anaesthetic and prepared the dart gun, before telling me he trusted me to shoot the lion. I hadn't expected to be launched in the deep end quite this soon. I had experience with shotguns and air rifles, but this was something completely different. We circled round the lion to get in closer without scaring it. I knew the best thing to do was aim and fire quickly, as hesitation would cause me to tremble and, more importantly, would show lack of confidence to Douw. He told me to aim at the shoulder muscles. Trying to appear relaxed, I raised the gun, sighted and fired. The gun hissed as the dart flew towards the lion, striking home perfectly in the triceps. The relief and exhilaration was immense as the lion sprang up and hobbled about twenty metres, showing us its injured back leg. Douw told me he could see my jugular pulsing as I fired.

Trude: The worry now was that the lion would find an inaccessible place to hide, so we had to follow it in the car. Soon it started to wobble and began to walk towards a hill with some bushes. It was lying on its side when we walked up to it, and Douw did the 'stick trick' (i.e. poke it with a stick and see if it wakes up to eat you). Luckily the lion was fast asleep and we all moved closer. It had scars and wounds everywhere, so it had obviously been in a lot of fights. The leg looked as though it had been injured for a long time, as all the muscles were fading away and the lion was very thin. Its ribs showed through its skin.

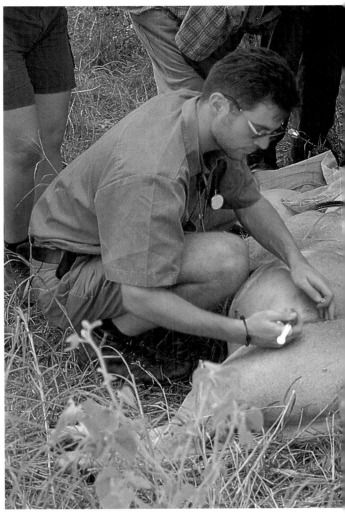

▼ Steve enjoying an opportunity to get really involved with some veterinary work. This lion was the first animal that Steve and Trude treated.

We carried it to the car, so it could be taken back to the camp. Carrying its head felt really strange, and its teeth were so white and big. Thinking about the type of damage they could do made me feel slightly nervous about carrying the lion in this way. I was glad he was knocked out. He was placed at the back of the pick-up, under the curious eyes of a lot of tourists taking photos.

On the way back we were monitoring the anaesthetic, by stopping every fifteen minutes to check that the lion was still asleep – but not too deeply. I wondered what would happen if he woke up while we were driving. I guessed he would be a very confused lion. However, we finally arrived back at the research camp, with the lion still asleep in the back.

Now it was time to take the samples we needed for research before we woke him up.

When I started to prepare to take the samples, Douw said to Steve that he must not let women take away his job! It was then I realized that it wasn't going to be easy working with Douw. Kruger National Park, is a very male-dominated place, and everything is oozing with testosterone.

Douw has a very domineering personality, which doesn't help me warm to him at all. I haven't been in a teaching situation since college, and now we were very much back to square one, especially me, as I haven't had any experience with large animals. Suddenly I felt a bit ignored, as all communication seemed to be directed towards Steve, and not towards me. It was going to be difficult. I think it is better to be a person with testosterone in a place like this – unless you are Superwoman, of course.

I took a blood sample from a vein in the lion's leg, under the watchful eyes of Douw. I felt very much like a student again. I was really nervous about not getting the vein, although I take blood samples from tiny animals at home in England all the time. It was so strange to hold this massive leg that reminded me of a cat's, but which was obviously so much bigger. I got the blood sample with some encouraging words from Steve, who understood how I felt.

There aren't many female vets here, and I felt very aware of the fact when everyone was watching me. Taking a blood sample from a lion shouldn't be hard, but I wasn't used to being watched by so many people.

We also did a tuberculosis test before the lion was put back into a cage, where Steve brought him round with an antidote. I must confess, I felt slightly panicky about being in this very cramped cage with a lion that was about to wake up, so I literally sprinted out of the cage as soon as the antidote was in!

Steve: After dinner, I checked on our lion. It was so dark that I couldn't see whether any of the other cages were occupied. As I was staring at what looked like a pile of hay, it growled so deeply that it shook my chest. My eyes adjusted and I could make out a huge male lion staring out at me. I can't imagine what that sound and sight must be like when you're alone out in the bush.

Trude: During dinner we heard some loud noises. We saw massive dark shadows walking past the electric fence, and soon we heard twigs and trees breaking with loud cracks. In between, we heard a deep rumbling and the strange noises that elephants make. When we left, the headlights of the car caught a glimpse of a big young bull elephant hiding behind some bushes. There were two of them, looking very happy about what they had just done. I suppose you can compare these elephants to teenagers that are looking for fun and trouble without thinking about what they are doing. It's OK for them to behave like this in the wild, but in a village, where people rely on crops to make a living, it's a matter of life and death. Elephants can be very destructive if they are allowed to roam freely in populated areas. I suppose I can see why they are not always so popular among the locals, although I thought it was slightly amusing, especially as they had been trampling on the local golf course. Big footprints could be seen on the ground. I wonder if they had had a good game of golf. Golf-playing elephants? Teenagers do get into an awful lot of trouble!

Did you know?

An elephant's trunk contains up to 150,000 muscle fascicles, enabling it to be moved in all directions.

Day five

Steve: We arrived early at Douw's office this morning to be presented with a cloud of confused instructions. We eventually worked out that we would be moving two bull elephants from the park to another park in South Africa. They were the pair responsible for disturbing our dinner last night, and were becoming a nuisance around the village. A huge crowd had gathered, but Douw was nowhere to be seen. JJ explained that he was in a helicopter looking for the elephants and we were waiting for a signal from him. We all hushed when the radio crackled and Douw announced that the elephants had been spotted. Then it was wagons roll. Everybody piled into their vehicles and we sped off in a long convoy. The sense of expectation was palpable, even among the locals.

Trude: The plan was to send a fixed-wing plane to locate the elephants, and then a helicopter would follow. Douw would be able to dart them with a sedative from the helicopter. We got a message on the radio saying that the hooligans had been located, and shortly afterwards the helicopter took off. Soon we had confirmation that one had been darted, and we set off in the Land Rover. It all felt like a military operation. It was hard to get a grip on what was happening, as everything moved so fast. It all seemed so well organized, with everyone having their own tasks and responsibilities.

Steve: We turned off onto a small dusty track that had once been a railway line. We could hear the helicopter quite clearly as we drove along the track with the dust blowing around us. Then it appeared, just above the tree line, skipping left and right, in and

▲ Top: Watching from a distance as Douw, in the helicopter, darts the elephant and then steers it to a clearing.
Above: Steve and Trude's first encounter with an elephant.

out of view. JJ explained that Douw was using the helicopter to steer the darted elephant nearer the road. The convoy stopped as Douw called instructions through the radio. Looking up the track, we could see the helicopter clearly now, above the trees and to the left. Suddenly, without warning, the elephant lurched out of the trees about a hundred metres away from us. It stood there, swaying for a second, before crumpling to the ground with an almighty thud, audible even over the noise of the helicopter.

Everybody got out of their vehicles, but only when JJ had flipped the elephant's ear over its eye could we move closer. We moved in slowly and reverentially, stroking the thick grey skin and speaking in excited, hushed tones. I moved all round the animal, taking in as much as I could. It was so big. The skin was like the bark of an old oak tree punctuated with short, thick, bristled hair. The trunk was soft and flaccid and rumbled loudly when the elephant breathed. The tusks were smooth like polished rock. Douw appeared from the bush with a wry smile on his face. The sense of urgency was obvious as the Game Capture Team set about moving the various tractors and lorries needed to load the elephant onto the trailer. There was hardly any need for discussion as they got on with their tasks. This was a very well-drilled team.

Trude: It was hard to know what to do in such an unfamiliar situation. I decided to try to monitor the anaesthetic, although I wasn't at all sure how you do that in an elephant. I thought to myself that it couldn't be that different from other animals as the basics are the same, so I went over to its head to check its pulse in an ear vein. Not the cleverest thing I have done in my life. Douw looked at me and said, 'What are you doing?' in a very strong South African accent. I said I was monitoring the anaesthetic, and he just laughed. Being patronizing seems to be a part of his sense of humour, and you needed to be strong and cheeky to handle him. I have never been good in teaching situations anyway, so I lost the game with Douw. I was stupid enough to take it personally and started to feel intimidated by him.

Being so close to an elephant – I was literally leaning on it – was something very special. I have seen elephants in zoos before, but when you see them in their natural habitat they look so different, especially when they are lying down, snoring. The elephant's skin was incredibly thick and covered with dust. The trunk was heavy to lift, and had to have a little stick inserted at the end to keep the airways free. The elephant was breathing regularly and heavily, while the Game Capture Team were fitting chains and other equipment in order to slide it across to a platform that could be lifted onto a truck. This, in turn, would be driven to a loading vehicle, where the elephant would be loaded on with the help of cranes and other high-tech equipment.

▼ The Game Capture Team were impressive to watch as they manoeuvred the elephant in to the truck.

I took blood samples from the ear veins. They were as large as a cat's leg, but funnily enough, I still managed to stick the needle in the wrong way. I suppose I am not used to working with large animals at all, so I expect everything to be more difficult. In reality, getting a vein on an elephant should be easier than getting one on a kitten. After having taken the blood, which again was being kept for a database, I stood on the sidelines watching as this enormous animal was somehow transferred from the ground to the back of the truck. Then we drove him to the loading truck. The roads were full of holes and dips, and I was convinced that all of us, including the elephant, would slip off the vehicle.

Steve: We pulled onto the airfield, and in front of us was a huge transport trailer with a recovery box behind it. There was a tense moment as the elephant was carefully winched into the recovery box.

Trude: The antidote was injected and everyone jumped out of the box, closed the doors and waited. Soon there was movement inside which is amazing. Douw explained that when times are hard very few pups will survive, but when a pack is doing well, more of them will live longer. This litter looked very healthy.

Trude: Wild dogs are the most beautiful creatures I have ever seen, they have long sleek bodies with black, white and brown markings, thin faces and long tails. On the top of their heads are two enormous ears, designed to pick up sound from far away. They weren't bothered about the car at all, and soon a hunting pack came back with food for the pups. All the dogs seemed to gather round the returned hunters in the hope of getting a little snack. The pups appeared from the den, and soon there were about twenty dogs with the pups all around the car. They whimpered and whined a lot, and there was a lot of submissive behaviour from the subordinate females in the pack. Wild dogs have a very interesting group structure; they help the wounded and weak by bringing prey home. This is rare in the animal kingdom, where survival of the fittest is the rule.

Did you know?

Did you know? Wild dogs can run up to 65 kph. They are also good at long distances, maintaining up to 48 kph for 5 km.

Steve: It was incredible to see the interplay between the pack members. Only the top female (called the alpha female) mates at any one time, but the rest of the pack look after the litter as if they were their own. Whenever the pups were out of the den, there were always half a dozen dogs in sentry positions around the edges of the clearing. Douw pointed out a dog with a broken forelimb. It must have been broken for some time, as there was a huge callous forming. I couldn't help wanting to repair the limb, but Douw explained that, given time, it would heal on its own. Knowing when not to interfere is a part of his job that I think it would be hard for me to get used to.

Trude: Seeing the pups tumble about in the grass made me feel so privileged. Wild dogs are an endangered species, so we were very lucky to have seen this pack. I can't stop being amazed by how accustomed these animals are to cars and vehicles. Wild dogs have a bad reputation among the locals, and I don't doubt that they can be dangerous if you come across them on foot. There is a lot of effort being put into protecting wild dogs from being killed by humans, and from dying of diseases caught from domestic dogs. We filmed until one of the females decided there were dangers about and, in a fraction of a second, they were all gone.

Steve: This evening the team went for a night drive, leaving Andres and Matias to cook the food. It wasn't long before we came upon a pride of lions lying on the road. It is quite common for them to lie on the tarmac, as it holds the heat well into the night. Douw told us that prides have learnt to hunt using the road to stumble their prey, as it is very slippery for hoofed animals to run on. These lions allowed us to drive right up to them. I asked Douw what they would do if I got out of the cab and he said, 'Get out and see.' So I did. I was very nervous but I'm glad I did. As the door opened, they pricked up their ears. When I walked a few steps (they were on the other side of the vehicle from me) they leapt up and sped into the night.

Trude: Having heard Douw's story about man-eating lions, I couldn't look at these lions without thinking about what they are capable of doing. Some years ago, refugees used to cross over from Mozambique through the park. A lot of people disappeared, but nobody reported them missing because they were refugees, and their families didn't expect to hear from them anyway. One day a man arrived at the head-quarters in Kruger

▲ A view like this is what you need after a long day's work.

and reported that all his friends had been attacked and eaten by lions as they walked through the park in the middle of the night. He had been lucky, and had managed to run away. This is when the authorities first started to suspect that something was wrong, as humans are not normally on a lion's menu. Douw and his colleagues took several vehicles onto the tracks they knew these people must have walked on. They played a tape of people talking, and it wasn't long before several lions appeared in obvious hunting positions. Normally lions will run away if they hear human voices, but not this pride. They had become specialized in killing people, and who could blame them? Humans must be the easiest prey to catch in the world: we talk loudly, can't run fast

▲ Trude giving the wildebeest the reversal agent.

Steve: Next, we went to film the lion we had brought in two days ago, in its cage. We walked nervously to the cage front. The lion was lying still as we approached. We stood next to the bars talking quietly, when suddenly it turned from a quiet cat into a snarling monster. My heart leapt like a startled rabbit, followed quickly by the rest of my body. Teeth bared and eyes glued to us, it was impossible not to be intimidated by the lion. You don't get any idea of how imposing these animals are when you see them on safari, as they are usually disinterested and relaxed, but seeing this one tensed and aggressive brought home what perfect killing machines they are. We made a prompt exit, and it settled down again very quickly. The plan is to sedate it again tomorrow to read its tuberculosis test and then, if it's positive, give it a post-mortem after putting it down. I don't know what will happen if it is negative.

This afternoon was the start of the main event – the elephant immuno-contraceptive project. Immuno-contraception entails injecting a drug derived from pig ovaries into female elephants. This causes an immune response against the elephant's own ovaries. When the eggs are released from the ovary, they are covered with antibodies, which prevent the sperm from penetrating and fertilization taking place. It is painless (except for the injection), and has no known side-effects, unlike hormone implants that have been used in the past. The process also has the benefit of being totally reversible in most species. In Australia, it is even being researched for use in humans. One of the founders of the technique is Dr Jay Kirkpatrick, who has come over to Kruger from the United States to help with the project. He is a very friendly, unassuming man, who you can't help but like. Some of the elephants we had been tracking on our first day at Kruger were involved in the programme, and had been darted with the drug some months ago. The plan was to dart these elephants again and, using rectal ultrasound, see if they were pregnant and so determine whether the contraceptive had worked. My job was to operate the ultrasound machine for Dr Richard Fayrer-Hosken, a huge Zimbabwean, who works at an American veterinary college. I think Richard was a little surprised by how well I knew my way around an ultrasound machine, but I use one almost daily at home to examine cattle reproductive tracts. At one end of the machine is a probe, which is placed into the rectum. Another problem with elephants is that everything is so much bigger than the cattle the machine was designed for. This called for a little ingenuity. The team had fashioned a rather phallic-looking probe extension to enable us to go that little bit farther!

Trude: I was the lucky one who got to go in the helicopter to try to locate the elephant herd. I had mixed feelings about that, because I got the impression that Douw wasn't too keen for me to accompany him. I kept on smiling to the camera so that I looked like my usual happy self, but on the inside I felt really intimidated and nervous about having to interact with Mr Growler – which is the nickname I have invented for him. However, I was determined to enjoy the experience, and once I was in the front seat

▼ Trude trying to look relaxed as she prepares to take to the skies in her first helicopter trip.

and had fastened the safety belt, I felt OK. My only worry was my tendency towards being airsick, and that was the last thing I wanted to happen in front of Douw. As soon as we took off, I realized I would be fine, though, because a helicopter moves very differently from a plane.

The view from the air was stunning. I had a sudden urge to be sentimental, thinking how lucky I was to be able to experience this! But I decided to play it cool. I was smiling a lot inside, though. As we flew

further into the bush, keeping our eyes open for the elephants, we saw all kinds of other animals running underneath us. Soon, we saw a herd of elephants moving fast through the thick bush, and tried to get closer to see if these were the ones we were after. The big elephants were getting concerned about the noise above them, and now and then one of the cows turned around, lifted up her trunk and flapped her ears about, warning us not to come too close. It was the herd we were looking for. Suddenly we saw a leopard running in front of the elephants. I think he must have been scared out of his 'sleeping tree' by the noise. He ran fast, and then disappeared.

The idea was to get close enough to one female for Douw to dart her. It was amazing to see how the pilot manoeuvred the helicopter, trying to separate this elephant from the others. The elephant calves were running as fast as they could, their little trunks wobbling from side to side. They looked so cute and comical. The elephant cows were trying to protect the young ones, letting them run in the middle of the herd. Soon we got close to the female we wanted. Douw got in a brilliant shot, half hanging out of the helicopter door. You can't be very scared of heights when you do this, that's for sure! In other words, I wouldn't last long.

As soon as the dart had hit the elephant, it was important that we tried to make her run towards a suitable area where there were not too many bushes or hills. The pilot gradually steered her towards a clearing, not far from the road, where the rest of the unit were now waiting. Now and then the elephant turned around flapping her ears to try to scare us off, then rushed through more bushes. She was getting more and more wobbly, and once out into the open space, she fell over. The vehicles were coming up already, and we prepared to land the helicopter. As we were running out of the helicopter, I started to worry about the rest of the herd, as I had heard stories about them returning to find out what was happening to their mate. I was running alongside Mr Growler. Unfortunately, I accidentally called the calves 'babies' ... big mistake. I was told grumpily by Douw that these were *not* babies, they were calves! Oops. It's at times like that you just want to be somewhere else. I was starting to realize that it was a no-win situation for me with Douw, unless I could impress him by lifting one of the elephants with one arm, or grow a beard and a lot of body hair!

Steve: The first elephant fell next to a clearing. I jumped out of our vehicle and walked straight into a 'wait-a-bit' bush, so called because it has thousands of barbs that cling to your clothes and skin. The only way out was to remove them one by one, which was difficult with my hands caught as well. I set up the ultrasound machine as Richard administered an enema to the elephant. To be able to see the screen in the sun, Richard and I were covered by a small canopy, which made for a very humid environment. We were joined from time to time by JJ, who couldn't help laughing at what we were doing. The first elephant was pregnant – this wasn't a surprise, as she hadn't been treated with the drug. The foetus was only 4 centimetres by 4 centimetres, so was very early on in its development.

Did you know?

Hannibal crossed the Alps with 40 African elephants.

Trude: I was taking blood samples – I managed to do it fine this time – and monitoring the anaesthesia. The aim was to find out if this elephant was pregnant. Meanwhile Steve and Richard were moving frantically inside their little green tent, trying to manoeuvre their rude-looking scanning probe.

▼ Once an elephant is sedated it needs careful monitoring until the reversal agent is given.

After a lot of panting and sweating, an image appeared on the monitor screen: an elephant foetus. I stuck my head under the tent to have a look. To be honest, it looked like a white blob that was moving a bit. However, she was pregnant, and would be a mother in twenty two months.

Steve: We packed up and got into the vehicles as Douw made ready to bring the elephant round. While we were scanning the pregnancy I was engrossed in the science, but as she rose to her feet and walked into the bush, I felt quite sentimental.

Day seven

Steve: I had my first-ever ride in a helicopter this morning. Douw and I set off from the airfield, with Barry our pilot, to dart

▲ Steve really gets stuck in!

some more female elephants. As we skimmed across the bush, Douw spotted a black rhino and asked Barry to turn round so that I could see it.

When we found the group we were interested in, we got very low over the bush, sweeping in to identify the animals we needed. Douw hung out of the door in the back as we manoeuvred over the backs of the adults, and darted the two females with collars on that we had spotted. Barry could get the helicopter within three metres of the elephants, which made Douw's job much easier. Once the elephants had been darted, Barry shepherded them gently towards a convenient spot for the ground team. When they had dropped, he then moved the rest of the herd away so the team could work safely. Within minutes of the darting, we landed on a track close to the two elephants and were swiftly joined by the rest of the team.

Today I have been to work! Administering an enema on an elephant is a memory that won't leave me for some time. I will return to the UK with Africa in my heart, hair and clothes. Elephant dung consists of large dry balls of fibre, complete with ten-centimetre thorns from acacia trees. I was amazed how these thorns could get all the way through an elephant's gut, especially as they penetrated my hands so easily. Once I had removed as many balls as I could, I had to pass a hosepipe as far forward as possible. The pressure on my arm was immense, and created a ring of bruising around my shoulder.

Trude: Steve had been given the task of doing an enema on the elephant, which he obviously enjoyed. It annoyed me a bit at first that I wasn't even considered, but to be fair, I think they knew how physically hard it was to do. I am strong, but I can't compete with Leonard! Watching Steve doing the enema, I realized that you really needed a lot of strength for the operation, as the faecal

balls were large and difficult to get out of the rectum. Steve was sweating and smiling. We called him 'faecal boy'! It was starting to heat up, and I wasn't envious of Steve having to stay under the tent, with his arm stuck up an elephant's bottom.

Steve: Over the day we got into a good routine and could relax a little. One of the elephants dropped very awkwardly, across a small river from the vehicles, and we had to race back and forth with all the gear, which was very tiring. In total we scanned five elephants and only one of them was pregnant. This was acceptable, because it was just over a year since the elephant was

▲ Having successfully administered the enema, Steve checks the ultra-sound to see whether the elephant is pregnant.

▲ Steve and Trude set off for their first cross-country trip in the newly customized vetmobile.

last injected, and the contraception should have started to wear off by now. This didn't stop Richard and I telling JJ that one of the other elephants was pregnant. We even faked an ultrasound picture, which I showed him. He was so crestfallen and dejected, we had to put him out of his misery and told him the truth. He cursed us to hell and back, while we just killed ourselves laughing at him. Douw was very happy, as things were going smoothly.

Day eight

Steve: Before we left Kruger, we discovered that the lion we had caught earlier in the week was negative for tuberculosis, but because of the extent of its injuries it had been put to sleep, rather than trying to treat the leg. Nobody likes losing a patient, but it happens to everybody at some point.

Trude: I think we both felt a bit surprised, maybe me more than Steve, as my work is with individual animals, and I am always trying to save lives if possible. Here the principles are different. To intervene with an individual animal in the wild is unethical, as nature must be allowed to take its course. You should only intervene if you think you can gain some knowledge that can help all wildlife, such as in this case. The tests had revealed that the lion was negative for tuberculosis, and nothing dramatic showed up in the blood samples. His records will be kept in a database. Databases are invaluable in case of an outbreak of disease. You can track back and see if there have been any abnormalities in the past which could indicate where and how the disease started.

Steve: Douw gave Trude, Michael and I bracelets made from elephant hair, which looks and feels like plastic wire. He said goodbye in turn to everybody, but when he shook my hand he said quite seriously, 'I know I'll be seeing you here again.' He was right. I will go back someday.

Driving out of the gate I felt a twinge of sadness about leaving, because I'd made some good contacts and also some friends. I also felt a touch of apprehension about what we would be facing next in Zimbabwe.

I was looking forward to driving the vetmobile across southern Africa though. It is a six-wheeled Land Rover with a built-in kitchen and veterinary store. It really is a huge vehicle, and it feels like it behind the wheel. Also, the gearbox is a bit random! After about ten minutes, something exploded under my feet. There was a huge bang followed by some nasty knocking noises so we had to take it steady before stopping overnight at a lodge north of Kruger.

CHAPTER 2

Zimbabwe

Day one

Steve: The landscape we drove through this morning looked very much like Arizona, with long, straight, undulating roads and huge rocky outcrops rising out of the plains. After an hour or two, making good time, we came to a crossroads and Andres decided at the last second to take a left to get some fuel. The vetmobile's not-too-wonderful brakes, coupled with the gearbox completely refusing me access to any of its gears, made for an interesting corner on three wheels, and when I pulled into the station I realized that the gear stick was no longer attached to the gearbox. Andres started swearing like a trooper, then burst into laughter. He swiftly organized Matias to go ahead and find us a Land Rover dealer in the next town, and sorted out a tow rope between the Land Rover and the vetmobile.

Trude: We had to be towed to the nearest town where we found Terry the mechanic, a lovely old man, about half the size of Steve, with a lot of bushy white hair and wearing a long blue coat. He knew absolutely everything there was to know about Land Rover engines. The vetmobile looks good, but doesn't seem to work well on these roads. I suppose it all adds to the adventure. Steve is enjoying every single minute of it; he knows a lot about engines, which is fortunate. I hate to be so girlie, but I haven't got a clue about them. I enjoy speed and nice cars but I am afraid that when it comes to knowing the anatomy of the car … Luckily, we didn't need to change the whole gearbox. Thanks to Terry the magic mechanic, we could head on.

There were small villages scattered along the road. The scenery reminded me of the film *Gorillas in the Mist*: a lot of green trees on hills and box-like houses gathered in villages. The rain never seemed to stop, although it looked a bit lighter on the horizon, and we were all waiting for the vetmobile's next breakdown.

Finally we arrived at the border. We had been told to be careful as a lot of people are out to rob you and take whatever they can. We stayed in the vetmobile most of the time, only getting out to have our passports stamped. I felt really unsafe. It felt like we were surrounded by vultures, just waiting for us to relax so they could steal from us. People were even looking into the cars, obviously trying to assess whether or not we had anything valuable to steal. I was glad we had Andres and Matias with us. They knew just what to do and what not to do.

We arrived at the hotel late at night, having passed a dead hippo next to the road and experienced a lot of suicidal donkeys trying to jump in front of the vetmobile.

No one tells you about how much travelling is involved when you do filming trips like this. It is an excellent opportunity for us to see a lot more of the countries, and also to learn about each other properly. Steve and I didn't really know each other well before we started filming this series. At college we only knew each other by name, and then we were thrown together when we did our first trip together for the *Holiday* programme. The long drives are a good opportunity to talk, and we have had lots of good conversations. However, anyone who knows me and Steve, or sees the series, will know how different we are as people. I suppose that's why we were put together on this project in the first place. Steve is an action man, while I am more cautious and careful. He can be extremely confident in the most strange situations, while I am almost shy sometimes. We talked about how much our lives have changed since we started the filming. I think I would say that I haven't changed at all, but that my career prospects have.

Day two

Steve: This morning started a little later than usual, which was very welcome after such a long day yesterday. We continued north at around 9.00 am, before stopping to film some of the spectacular scenery. The area we stopped in was awesome, with flat, dusty plains and huge, round rock hills dotted here and there. They looked like huge pebbles that had been dropped into a sandpit.

Trude: The scenery has changed a lot since we crossed the border. There are more mountains, and in the valleys there are small huts scattered around. The green vegetation makes everything look very fresh. When we stopped to do some filming, small children gathered around the car begging for things like pens and oranges. They were a greedy lot, and giving them one thing caused a lot of fighting among them. They looked so happy, though, that I think the begging was more of a fun thing they did, not something necessary to survival. They were smiling and laughing all the time. It's amazing to see how people with so little can be so happy and laid-back.

Steve: Our hotel for the night is the Great Zimbabwe Hotel, which is adjacent to Great Zimbabwe, an ancient ruin. The word 'Zimbabwe' is thought to come from the ancient dialect for 'stone houses', and the country is named after this spectacular site. Early European explorers considered the immense stone fortress far too advanced for the indigenous people, preferring to believe that it was built by the Greeks, or by another foreign culture. More recent research has led to the accepted theory that Africans were the architects of this immense structure, and it has become a very symbolic piece of African heritage. The fortress walls are made of stone without any mortar, and look very similar to dry-stone walls in Lancashire, except that these are about twelve metres high. The ruins were very impressive, and we spent some time exploring them.

Trude: You could almost feel the prehistoric atmosphere. Once there were 20,000 people living here. If you closed your eyes, and listened to the wind blowing through the stones, you could imagine all the people running about, in and out of the ruins. Some baboons on the other side of the valley decided to scream out on several occasions, making me jump. Otherwise it was very quiet. We did some filming inside the ruins, then we put up the vetmobile ready to cook a meal. We had the most amazing view.

▼ The vetmobile attracted a lot of attention as Steve and Trude drove north through Zimbabwe.

Day three

Trude: We had a long drive north today. We spent a lot of time filming the vehicle on the way up, and every time we stopped we were stared at. The sun is out today, which is more like it!

Steve: Before we left we stopped at the gate of our hotel where there were about thirty stalls, each with more than a hundred wooden and stone carvings laid out in rows. I had set my heart on a stone rhino. Rhinos are so distinctive, and the emotions I felt seeing them in the wild for the first time were strong enough to be brought back just by thinking about them. Being so close to these rare and enigmatic creatures has left a very powerful impression on me. I wanted an anatomically correct carving and after some searching I found exactly the right one. The horn was long and polished and the whole thing was cool to the touch, and weighed a surprising amount for its size. The stall owner wanted clothes rather than money – jeans or shirts – of which I didn't have many to spare. We shook on a pair of shorts, a T-shirt and 120 Zimbabwe dollars.

Day four

Steve: This morning I felt as if we had been driving for ever. We have literally driven straight across Zimbabwe towards the north. But at last we have arrived at Matusadona National Park, where we will spend the next few days.

Trude: We met Chris Foggin, the vet, at the gate. He is very different from Douw – a quiet-spoken man, with a witty sense of humour. Straight away I felt more comfortable than I had at Kruger National Park. Chris seems much more mellow, and actually looked at both of us when he spoke to us, unlike Douw.

Steve: The road into the park was extremely rough, and it took some time to get to Lake Kariba. In fact the lake is a reservoir formed by the damming of the Zambezi river. It is a hydroelectric dam, and provides power for both Zimbabwe and Zambia, as the river forms part of the border between the two countries. Matusadona National Park lies along the shore of the lake and is unique because of its abundance of water; the game there is numerous. We finished today's journey by speedboat to Kipling's Lodge, which was spectacular.

▼ Rounding up the rhinos to be fed and weighed each morning needed an expert hand.

Trude: The lodge is fantastic, like a fairy-tale village, with thatched roofs and all the chalets facing the lake. Nearby, hippos rested in the water, grunting and squealing all the time. This is the most romantic place I have ever seen in my life. I will have to get married and come back for a honeymoon …

Day five

Steve: I was very confused at my 5.30 am wake-up call. The first job of the day was to feed the rhino calves. These are black rhinos that have been taken from their mothers to encourage further breeding in the adult population. When they are born they weigh 35–40 kilograms (about the weight of an adult rottweiler), and it was with this in mind that I approached the boma where they are kept.

Trude: We arrived, very excited, at the rhino bomas. Our first meeting with the nursery group was hilarious. I was expecting some small, friendly 'babies', but what met us was very different. First, two of them poked their heads around the corner of the bomas, and we all said how cute they were. Next, two galloping waist-high tanks turned the corner, and started to nudge us. I found myself trapped up against a wall, with this incredibly powerful beast peering at me through some very thick, leathery folds. I couldn't believe how strong they were. Chris was shouting to me to be firm. I tried as best as I could, slapping the rhino around the nose. She just ignored me totally, and kept on pushing me into the boma wall. When she finally decided I wasn't going to play, she galloped away. I was left slightly bewildered by what had happened, and with some impressive bruises on my legs.

However, after the initial shock we all got sticks to 'Zorro' them with. Mbeze and Cleopatra were the worst animals: typical girls, moody and grumpy. Mbeze kept on trotting around squealing for more food, and in between she would charge after one of us. She certainly made us move. I have never seen Dudley our soundman running so fast before.

▼ It was an amazing experience to be able to get so close to the rhino calves.

These rhinos were between six and eighteen months old. Most had been taken away from their mothers to decrease the calving interval, in an attempt to increase the number of black rhinos in Zimbabwe – the same sort of scheme that was being adopted with the white rhinos in South Africa. Mbeze was found with her skinny mum, who had been injured by poacher's snares. She couldn't look after her calf very well, hence the decision to take Mbeze from her.

It was amazing to see their perky, cheeky eyes peering at you in between the attacks. Rhinos have strange, long faces and short stumpy legs. We watched them being fed and weighed and then they all went out to browse. They were suckling from a bottle, just like other animal babies. You can imagine that these rhinos form very strong bonds with their keepers. I took the temperature of one of them, so now I can say I have seen a rhino's bottom at close hand as well. How is it that vets always end up at that end of an animal?

Seeing these animals up close in their natural habitat, being able to touch them and slap them, is something I will never forget. The black rhino is virtually extinct: very few people have actually seen them, let alone experienced four calves dancing around wanting to play. A moment to remember for the rest of my life.

Rhino

Size: There are two species of rhino – black and white. The white rhino is the larger, with the males reaching 1.8 m in height and 2.5 tonnes in weight. The black rhino males only reach 1.6 m in height and 1.3 tonnes in weight.

Life span: Their expected life span is about 30 years, but the rhinos are always threatened by poaching.

Distribution: Hunting and poaching have decimated numbers of both species. The black rhino is the more endangered of the two species. They are now only really found in well-protected parks.

Behaviour: White rhinos are sociable animals and can be found in herds. Black rhinos are mainly solitary with associations rarely tolerated. Both species are slow breeders, only producing young every 2–3 years.

Diet: White rhinos have wide, square lips and feed by grazing, so are commonly found on open grasslands. Black rhinos have a prehensile pointed upper lip used for delicate browsing. They are found in bush areas feeding on branches and twigs.

Steve: The rest of the morning was spent interviewing Chris as we drove around the park in the vetmobile. When we came back towards the shore, we found the rhinos grazing on the airstrip, so we stopped to feed them. They were a lot quieter than they had been earlier and took small branches out of my hand, which was amazing considering the havoc they were wreaking this morning. Cleopatra allowed me to get almost lip to lip, as I offered her small twigs from green bushes. She stood there quietly munching away as I played with her lip, explaining to the camera that the lip is one of the main differences between white and black rhino. The small, pointy prehensile upper lip enables the black rhino to select their food carefully; the wide, flat lips of the white rhino are used for grazing. I felt incredibly privileged to be so intimate with Cleopatra. Face to face, she reminded me of a triceratops dinosaur, especially when I looked down at her three-toed feet. We must have spent an hour with her standing there. When Cleopatra had had enough, she made her way down to the water's edge, through some trees, with the others. We tried to follow them, but ended up either losing them or being charged by them. Dudley had to have some firm words with one that was trying to destroy his sound equipment.

Did you know?

Rhinos are very nimble and can change direction quickly, even at speeds of up to 50 kph.

Trude: We were keeping an eye on Mbeze when we heard some twigs breaking in the forest. We looked up and saw several buffaloes. Buffaloes are one of the most dangerous species in Africa and can kill people. Panic broke out. We had the lake with crocodiles on one side and the forest with buffaloes on the other side; we were trapped. I kept asking Michael what we were going to do, but he didn't know. The problem was that the buffaloes wanted to get to the water where we were. When we all thought we would have to jump in the water or start to run, we heard a squeal and a lot of twigs breaking. There was Cleopatra, the youngest rhino, chasing the buffaloes away. Her tail stood straight up like a little flag, and she was puffing and panting, trying to look big and scary. She charged after them into the forest, then returned to us in the same posture, as if showing off, trotting around us at an incredible speed. I suppose she regarded this as her territory, and would not stand for the buffaloes intruding into her little area. We were all so relieved, and couldn't believe what had just happened. Rescued by a rhino: cool or what!

Day six

Steve: The main event was going to the crocodile farm this afternoon. The farm owner, Charles, met us at his house. There was an orphaned buffalo calf in his garden, which Charles's wife Julie had recently rescued from a ditch full of slurry. Since being rescued, it had developed quite bad diarrhoea. Julie was keen to tap us for information about getting the calf well again. It looked like a nutritional problem, and we reasoned that the calf should, hopefully, respond to a change in diet. It was strange dealing with sick calves all the way out here, but at least it was a problem I was on firm ground with. Unlike the problem I was about to face.

Trude: Charles showed us around the farm. I was astonished to see all the tanks with the small crocodiles; and then there were the pens with the bigger ones. There were crocodiles everywhere, and when you looked into one pen, there where so many that they all looked like one big moving animal. Most of them were lying still in the sun, but when we walked past, they all moved at the same time into the shallow water.

Steve: The main output from the crocodile farm is skin. It takes more than two years to get the crocodiles to the right size, and the skin has to be free from blemishes. About half of the crocodiles are rejected because of imperfections in the skin. Most of the blemishes will grow out, but this means keeping them for another six months. Their size is directly related to age, and at birth they are a matter of inches long.

▼ Even the young crocodiles had a menacing look when they were seen en masse.

Trude: The scariest pen was the one for the breeding stock. The crocodiles there were massive, about three or four metres long. Charles asked one of the workers to walk into the pen, to demonstrate how quickly the crocodiles could move. I thought the worker smiled rather nervously, and looked a bit reluctant, but he still jumped into the pen with a broom. The worker touched one croc with the broom. It threw itself around, roared and opened its mouth wide before it slid into the water. We all jumped, because the contrast was amazing; the speed with which this animal moved was scary. The worker grinned as soon as he knew he was safe. These people clean the pens every day. Hygiene is of paramount importance, as there is such a high density of animals in one place that outbreaks of disease will spread very quickly.

Steve: Two handlers got into a pen and set about catching the crocs. The technique is apparently simple – sneak up behind the croc and grab it by the nose, using only a small square of sacking for protection. Charles lay down the gauntlet by telling me to jump in and give a hand. I leapt in readily enough, but as I approached the first croc, it spun round and lunged at me, roaring and hissing like a demonic creature. I retreated swiftly, but Charles was having none of it. Having spotted one of his staff dragging one of these beasts through the water towards me, he encouraged me to give him a hand. I managed to get hold of a hind limb and helped lift the croc onto the low wall where we could examine it. It was then that I saw the crowd of staff Charles had around him, having a good laugh at my efforts. I had noticed that the crocs were quieter when in the water, so when Charles said I could have another go after the pen was flooded, I didn't refuse. Nevertheless, I still had serious misgivings about whether I could really grab one of them by the dangerous end.

▲ Another new experience: performing a post-mortem on a young crocodile.

Trude: My next task was to perform a post-mortem on a crocodile. I have never seen a crocodile on the inside before, and have never been taught about their anatomy, so this was a learning experience for me. We had some crocodiles that had been found dead, and it is important to establish the cause of death to avoid any epidemics. I worked my way through one crocodile. It was difficult! They were so different from the domestic species I am used to. However, after a lot of cutting, I had some specimens ready for Chris. I was struggling to open its skull, so much so that he had to help me. A lot of the workers gathered around to watch us. They must have thought we were mad to film a crocodile being cut open. We suspected that the crocodile had died of meningitis.

Steve: When we returned to the pen, it was flooded to about mid-calf height, apart from the troughs, which were thigh level now. One of the staff lent me a pair of wellies, and I hopped into the tank. Charles was giving me instructions and encouragement. I was no longer aware of the audience: all of our team and about twenty of Charles's staff. My heart was going like the clappers as I started to stalk my first potential catch of the day. It eyed me very suspiciously as I approached it from the rear, hands just in the water, with my piece of sacking poised. The croc glided along, trying to gauge whether I was to be trusted or not, and I followed, gaining slowly. As soon as I thought I was close enough, I lunged for its head and felt my hands glide over the end of its nose. It had slipped backwards and away before I knew anything. A big gasp from the crowd was followed by Charles selecting my next quarry.

I made my way towards my new target. As I got closer it started to move up the wall, and I knew I only had one chance at it, so I moved in as near as I could before mounting my attack. I knew I had aimed too close to the end of the nose, last time, so elected for a neck grab. But although it was a bigger area to grasp, it wasn't possible to hold its jaw shut at the same time. It thrashed from side to side as I pinned it down with all my strength. I was acutely aware of its numerous teeth as it tried to spin round and remove my calf muscles. I got one leg on either side of it and held on for dear life, but I knew I had to grab the mouth if I wanted to get it under

Crocodile

Size: There are three species of crocodile in Africa with the largest being the Nile crocodile which can grow up to 6 m in length and 1 tonne in weight.

Life span: Huge myths around the life span of crocodiles are often heard. The oldest recorded animal was 115 years old when it died in a Russian zoo.

Distribution: Crocodiles are well adapted to live in salt and fresh water and are found in west, central and east Africa.

Behaviour: Contrary to popular belief crocodiles can make caring mothers. The female Nile crocodile fasts for 3 months while guarding her buried nest of eggs. When they hatch she carries them to water in her mouth to wash them.

Diet: Young crocodiles feed on insects while on land. As they grow they move into the water to take fish, birds and small mammals. The biggest crocodiles are capable of catching and killing adult wildebeest.

control. Timing and accuracy were crucial to prevent me being badly bitten. Acting more on reflexes than anything else, I let go of its neck, whipped my hands onto its nose and felt its jaws come together. My fingers got a good grip under its chin and I pulled its head clear of the water. It stopped struggling right away, and I knew I had done it. The relief on my face was obvious, and I got a small round of applause from all the onlookers. I had picked a monster all right: it was about two metres in length, and I was only just able to cart it over to the edge, where Charles was grinning nearly as much as I was. I found out later that he had been wagering with the site manager as to whether I was going to get bitten, and at one point both had thought I was going to. It was undoubtedly the biggest buzz I've ever had in my life. I can't wait until my brothers see this – in fact, I can't wait until I see it, because I can't believe I did it.

Trude: Having seen Steve and the keepers catching the crocodiles, and seeing how nervous Steve was, I decided to abandon altogether the idea of being macho and trying to catch one myself. This was not the time to be a feminist, this was the time to pull out the lipstick and giggle. I WAS NOT GOING TO TRY TO CATCH ONE OF THESE BEASTS!

Day seven

Steve: We left Kipling's Lodge for good this morning. Trude started the driving, and Chris came in our vehicle to be filmed on the way.

Did you know?

Crocodiles' teeth are continually replaced, with an old animal getting through up to 50 sets in its lifetime.

Trude: Driving the vetmobile is a very new thing for me, and I am really learning as we go along. Today I had to drive it on extremely bumpy roads, with sandy banks and water crossings. One part of the driving I thought was essential was to drive fast and so to build up momentum. So today I hammered along, not knowing I was actually driving a bit too fast. I had seen Steve drive, and he drives very fast; being in the mood to learn, I tried to do everything Steve did, but I forgot that he has more experience than me.

I noticed Chris looking a bit nervous at times, but in general I thought I had control. It was when we hit a sandbank that things went wrong. I knew I needed a low gear to get through, but I managed to choose the wrong track somehow, and lost

▲ Catching a crocodile was the biggest buzz Steve had ever had.

momentum. The vetmobile sank into the sand and we were stuck. I was very angry with myself, because things had been going so well up until then, (well, that's what I thought, anyway). I had messed it up, and we had to get the winch out. In the process of pulling the winch over to an appropriate tree, I managed to cut my leg on a sharp plant leaf. That was it for me. I was so fed up, and started moaning away to Steve. Steve took on the role of Dr Leonard, and cleaned my 'massive' cut – OK, it wasn't that big, but it was big enough for me to want to make a point of it!

Steve: Chris was taking us to Fothergill, which is a small peninsula where there is a high prevalence of floppy trunk disease. This is a horrific disease which causes elephants' trunks to become paralysed. It starts at the tip and progresses up the length of the trunk. It has a very debilitating effect, as the trunk is used for feeding and drinking. In the early stages of the disease, the elephants adapt very well, using the body of the trunk as opposed to the digits on the tip. As it worsens, they learn to flick their trunks over branches to bring them to their mouths, and they wade into deep water to drink. Eventually, however, the paralysis becomes so great that feeding and drinking become very difficult, and the animals start to lose condition rapidly and die. In the park they are culled on humane grounds before the condition becomes too severe. There are a number of theories about the cause of the disease. Chris is involved in vegetation studies around Fothergill, as the disease is more evident in this area. He has also taken tissue samples from affected elephants to see what changes are present. These biopsies are taken in the field under sedation and local anaesthetic.

We were met by Nettie, a postgraduate who is doing some research into cheetahs in the park. She, along with other researchers and guides from the lodges, keeps Chris informed of affected elephants and suspect cases in the area. Chris relies heavily on volunteers such as Nettie, as he has no staff of his own to help him in his research. She told us the whereabouts of an elephant with early signs of floppy trunk disease, and Chris was keen to take a look.

Trude: After a long search with a lot of hanging about in the bush, we finally managed to locate him: an old bull elephant with big tusks. Bull elephants are very often found on their own, while the females keep in matriarchal groups consisting of cows, calves and juveniles. It felt very different to be on the ground, compared to being in a helicopter. You become very aware of the size of these animals, and your own very small size. We were hiding behind some bushes, but had to make sure the wind was blowing in the right direction so that the elephant wouldn't be able to smell us. They can't see very well, but they can pick up a foreign scent from miles away.

He was massive, moving very slowly. His trunk looked thinner than it should have been and he was struggling to manoeuvre the leaves into his mouth. The trunk is really like an extra arm, incredibly muscular and flexible. This didn't look good. We decided to dart him, whereupon he started to move into the bush. We drove along the shore to follow him, and when we thought we would be able to get close enough, we jumped out of the vehicle.

▲ The effects of floppy trunk disease could be seen at the tip of the bull elephant's trunk.

Steve: We set up close to where the elephant had stopped, and Chris made up the dart. He was going to let me shoot, but as we got close the bull started moving off, so he took the shot.

Trude: There was a short thump and then the elephant was rushing forward, startled. He turned around, as if looking for where the noise had come from from. It was probably the noise more than the dart that had scared him. I held my breath as he was still looking for something moving. It was crucial at this point that he didn't charge, as we were at least one minute's run away from the vehicle. My heart was thundering inside my chest; I am sure he could hear it. I think this was one of the scariest experiences we have had so far.

After a minute or so, the elephant turned around and started to walk. He soon began to wobble, and then we heard a thump as he hit the ground. When we were sure he was properly asleep, we ran forward to start to prepare the biopsy site. Steve was given the responsibility of taking blood samples, fitting the radio collar and monitoring the anaesthetic, which is very important. The type of drug we were using could cause respiratory arrest if not monitored carefully.

Steve: I hadn't got a watch, so I had to count the seconds in my head. Nettie put a radio collar on the elephant. She needed a hand to pass the collar under the sleeping elephant's neck. Chris told us to tighten it up one notch. Nettie and I thought it would be too tight, but we did as Chris asked. I had to take blood samples and was struggling to find the right blood tube holder, when Chris asked how the breathing was. I estimated the next respiratory cycle. Chris turned to Nettie and asked her to time it as well. She timed it on her watch, and I was well out. I'd messed up and I knew it. In fact everybody knew it. Chris didn't say anything, but I wouldn't like to describe the look I got from Nettie. Chris gave the

Elephant

Size: Elephants are the largest land mammals. There are two subspecies of African elephant – the 'forest elephant' and the 'plains elephant'. The plains elephant is the larger of the two and can reach 3.7 m in height and weigh around 6 tonnes. The skin alone can weigh 1 tonne and the heart 40 kg.

Life span: Elephants live for around 50–60 years. They have six sets of teeth over a lifetime and when the last fall out they cannot eat and therefore starve.

Distribution: Elephant distribution has been well documented over the years, and once included all of Africa, right up to the Mediterranean coast. They are no longer found in north Africa. They can survive in a variety of habitats but do need access to permanent water (except for the desert elephants of Namibia). Elephants don't have sweat glands so rely on bathing to keep cool.

Behaviour: Elephants live in herds of between 6 and 30 animals. The herd is lead by the eldest female, called the matriarch. Males leave the herds at the age of 14 years and roam around on their own. An elephant's eyesight is not very good but they have a very good sense of smell, and with their mobile trunk can smell at various heights and in different directions. Communication between elephants is by making very low rumbling noises that are thought to be heard by other elephants over many kilometres.

Diet: The trunk enables the elephant to take advantage off many different types of vegetation. They eat grasses, bushes, branches from trees and bark depending on the season and locality. Elephants decimate large areas of woodland by felling trees and also by stripping all the bark.

elephant some more drugs to adjust the level of sedation and we carried on. My stomach felt like an empty pit, and I found it hard to keep working. I wanted to start walking until I reached the UK and not look back.

Trude: I started to scrub the trunk and the operation site with Chris. The whole trunk was vibrating. The elephant was snoring really loudly! I couldn't really hear a lot because I was sitting next to its mouth, and had my hair blow-dried every time it exhaled!

The trunk was difficult to scrub up, with all the folds and the fact that it moved every time the elephant exhaled. Moreover, these were bush conditions, and the last time I had operated was on a cat in Bristol, under very sterile conditions. However, we soon had the site ready, and I was ready to cut the skin with my scalpel. From that moment I concentrated fully on what I was doing. Around me, Steve was struggling with the collar and trying to count the breaths at the same time. I tried to stay focused and be as quick as possible. The skin was really tough to cut through – what a contrast to hamster skin! I was actually shaking, because I knew I had to be quick and Chris was watching. I am very bad in teaching situations, but on this occasion I had to pull myself together and pretend this was just like operating at home. Once I was through the skin, there was a lot of blood. I tried to swab as much as I could so that I could see what I was cutting, and slowly I managed to cut free a piece of the muscle that contained some nerves. Once that was done, I started to stitch the site up. I could hear in the background that Steve had counted the breaths wrongly, so the elephant was actually breathing more slowly than we wanted it to. Chris was getting a bit stressed and wanted me to hurry up, so that we could reverse the elephant's sedative as soon as possible.

I had a couple of stitches left when Michael shouted, 'Elephant! Elephant!' I was concentrating, so I didn't look up. Apparently, it wasn't that Michael had only just discovered that it was an elephant we were operating on, there was another elephant that had apparently stumbled across us, and was standing about twenty metres away, looking at us. He must have wondered what on earth we were up to, and what we were doing with this elephant. Luckily, he didn't get any closer, but it was a very tense moment. Talk about working under pressure.

We were all so relieved, and my sentimental side surfaced. I was very touched by the whole operation – it was so incredibly beautiful and special to see the old bull elephant walk into the

▲ Trude performing the most unusual biopsy of her career, an elephant's trunk.

bush as if nothing had happened at all. And it's good to feel useful once in a while, to do some proper veterinary work. Hopefully the biopsy will contribute in some way towards finding a cure for floppy trunk disease. I was very happy and very encouraged at the end of our work today.

Steve: Trude finished her biopsy and the elephant was revived. When it stood up, it was obvious that the collar was too tight and Chris said he would knock the elephant down again next week and loosen its collar. It made me feel a little better that even someone as experienced as Chris makes the odd error. With that in mind, I went and apologized to Chris about fouling up. He seemed OK about it, and this helped me relax a little.

Day eight

Steve: We had a very early start this morning, although we did have a moonlit boat ride across the lake to ease us into the day. The stars were magnificent, and the planets were easy to see. The task of remaining dry occupied us for much of the journey because, as it got a little choppier, huge plumes of water shot into the boat. Gillian took the worst of it, and was thoroughly drenched by the time we arrived. Thankfully by then the sun had come up, and we dried off very quickly.

Our project today was to retrieve a wandering black rhino that had left the park boundaries. It was one of the first calves to be hand-reared in the park, and had only recently been released to fend for itself. Outside the park, rhinos are at risk of being killed by poachers. Chris told us that the trucks required to transport the rhino were not in good condition, and he was worried about being able to get the animal back quickly. The trucks left early this morning and we went to meet up with them just outside the park.

Trude: The rhino was last seen about a two-and-a-half-hour drive from Matusadona, near a village. The plan of action was to track and dart him and then transport him back. That might sound simple, but we soon realized that this was not going to be as easy as the Kruger operations we had seen.

We set off on a long and extremely bumpy road. Steve enjoyed the rally-driving, while Dudley and I were bobbing up and down in the back seat. We all started off very jolly, but ended up green-faced, and had to resort to travel-sickness tablets. Arriving at the site where the vehicles were supposed to be, we discovered that the trackers had set off in the bush *without* a radio, and that the fan belt of one of the vehicles had snapped. We were about to experience 'the African way'.

We hung around for several hours before we decided to abort the mission. We had been really geared up to catch this rhino, so

went ahead to see if Michael had rung the hotel on the satellite phone. We didn't know that Gillian and Michael were stranded in a village for hours before we decided to look for them. I think Michael was irritated that we hadn't gone back for him earlier, as there is a general rule that vehicles should all stay together.

After rescuing Gillian and Michael, we settled into the lodge, which was situated next to the Zambezi river. The first thing I noticed was that everything seemed so commercialized. It's strange how readily I resented this after having been in the bush.

Day twelve

Steve: This afternoon we made our way to the Zambezi bridge to check out the gorge and the falls. We walked across the bridge and it was magnificent. The height was staggering. The gorge walls were so straight they looked as though they were man-made. The muddy waters churned away below us as we came to the middle of the bridge and the jumping platform, from which people perform bungee jumps.

Trude: I can't stand heights at all, and I react with anger to other people who want to do things like bungee-jumping. I tried to look over the edge, but I felt nauseous, and was so scared after two seconds that my legs felt like lead weights. Steve thought that was funny, and kept on pretending to climb over the fence all the time. There was a bit of a discussion going on as to whether he should bungee-jump or not. I thought, surely it wouldn't be responsible of Michael to let him do it? What if something happened? They decided that Steve could take responsibility for his own actions, and that Michael would film the jump. I felt like a nagging mother, trying to talk him out of it.

Steve: I rushed off, paid my ninety American dollars at a small shack and ran back. By this time Michael was getting quite keen to film the whole thing. Dudley wired me up so he could record my screams. Norman, the guy managing the jumps, said Denis could come onto the platform if he wore a harness. This bungee-

▲ Steve preparing to bungee-jump over Victoria Falls – the second biggest buzz of the trip.

◀ The famous Victoria Falls exceeded both Steve and Trude's expectations in their size and beauty.

jump is the second highest in the world, at 110 metres. The free fall lasts for about four seconds, and the view is awesome. Usually you spend very little time waiting on the platform to jump, but I was there for a long time waiting for Denis to come up behind me. I was standing with my feet tied together and my toes hanging in the breeze. I made myself look down to appreciate the depth, and was surprised at how calm I felt. Denis came through onto the platform and almost knocked me off when he swung his camera into position. I didn't want to shout 'Geronimo' or anything too clichéd, but the only thing that came into my head was 'MOTHER!!!!' I leapt as far out as I could, and looked down at the massive amount of nothing between me and the river. The acceleration was immense, and all I could hear was the wind rushing in my ears. I regret not looking sideways on the way down, but all I saw was the water rushing towards me. Finally the cord tightened and I slowed down to a stop, still some considerable distance from the water. It was all rather gentle because of the length of the cord, and the rebounds gave me time to appreciate how far I had come. I was winched back up and made my way back to the bridge surface. It was a hell of a buzz, but as nervous as I was, it was nothing compared to getting into a pen full of crocodiles.

▼ Enjoying a more tranquil moment at the falls.

Trude: To get the best view of the falls, we had to cross over to the Zambia side. When we got there, there was a bit to walk before we could see the falls themselves. I must admit, I had assumed that they would be overrated, but they were the most impressive sight I have ever seen. I was astonished that it was so beautiful – so much water, so noisy! There was a rainbow, and there was water everywhere.

Steve: The volume of water is incomprehensible. We spent about an hour there walking and filming. At one point, you stand right at the edge of the gorge, where there's no fence, just slippery rock between you and the bottom. There is a small area of rainforest adjacent to the falls, because of the constant mist pouring upwards out of the gorge, and we were drenched. I couldn't believe that one kilometre from the tourist-ridden town was this unspoilt, awe-some natural phenomenon. I was struck with an amazing feeling of love for this continent. It is so beautiful, and the people are so friendly and welcoming. I have had so many incredible experiences and seen so many wondrous things, and I have only seen a fraction of what Africa has to offer.

Trude: On the way back we decided to catch a taxi; well, if you can call it a taxi. It's amazing to see what people do to earn a living here in Africa. These people earned theirs by taxiing tourists across the border, or to the border. The vehicles were just unbelievable. The one we took barely had four wheels, the doors were about to fall off and the driver started the engine by coupling some wires together. His seat had some fluffy lining here and there. He told us that this car was like his wife – old and tired; we laughed a lot. His car only started if his friend pushed it first!

Day thirteen

Trude: This morning we woke up for a nice breakfast. As we were eating, I was aware of some broken trees in the lodge garden, I'd heard them snap during the night. Apparently there had been some elephants in the neighbourhood. I suddenly realized that they were still around, behind where we were having breakfast, chomping away on a tree. Some tourists was getting very near them. Then the elephants calmly walked past us, into the lodge garden, molested another tree, and left. I was totally stunned that they had got so close to us. The lodge staff just had to watch as they destroyed the trees. I have never eaten breakfast under those kind of circumstances before. And probably never will again.

Steve: I spent much of the day at the market stalls buying more sculptures. I bought more rhinos and hippos, and an abstract human pose called 'The Thinker'. The big problem is that I won't want to give any of them away. Bartering was great fun, and the stallholders were really friendly and willing to have a laugh. 'No offer an insult' was the phrase used by one man, who then burst out laughing when I offered my first price.

We spent sunset on the Zambia side of the falls again, but this time off duty, without the cameras. We all had a few drinks and just enjoyed the falls.

CHAPTER 3

Botswana

Day one

Trude: Today we crossed the border to Botswana and then drove past cotton fields and lots of space on our way to Khutse Game Reserve. We even saw some ostriches. I was a bit worried during the journey that the vet here might be like Douw.

Steve: We are filming a giraffe translocation project. The giraffes are being moved from here to a wildlife reserve just outside Gabarone, because the giraffe population there was wiped out by an unknown disease. We arrived in the dark and only just found the camp site. We introduced ourselves to Pete Morkel. Pete is world-renowned for his work with African wildlife. He struck me instantly as a very relaxed and easygoing guy, and I am sure things will go smoothly. Puso Kirby, who speaks and looks like a surfer, is the manager from Mokolodi Nature Reserve, where we will be moving the giraffe to. Our camp hadn't arrived and it was a little embarrassing for us to admit that we had no tents or sleeping gear, especially as we were supposed to be feeding everybody as well. Thankfully, they had brought some provisions of their own and allowed us to share their meal. I had got a sleeping bag in my bag, and so I was set for the night. The rest of the team had to depend on donations of blankets and bedding, making up one huge bed on the ground which they all got in to. Michael hinted that I should give up my sleeping bag to Trude. I hinted back: no chance.

Day two

Steve: Last night was freezing. The others emerged warm from under their blankets, far better off than the people from whom they had borrowed them, who were walking around like blocks of ice. The sun soon rose and everybody thawed quickly enough.

Catching giraffes is no easy procedure. They don't handle the drugs too well when they are darted. If they get too low a dose, they run themselves to exhaustion and die, so they are given a lethal overdose, brought down quickly and revived. Timing is critical, and everybody has to know exactly what they are doing.

▲ As if in slow motion, the giraffes were spotting galloping along the horizon, closely followed by the helicopter.

Once darted from the helicopter, the giraffe has to be captured using ropes. Two men hold a length of rope in front of the running giraffe, like a finishing tape, for it to run into. Once it has been stopped, a second rope is wound round its ankles and pulled tight, to trip it up. This sounds easy, but involves two groups of people running opposite ways round the giraffe, trying not tangle themselves up in the rope. Pete acted as the giraffe for us to practise on and even with a stationary target it was a little chaotic. Pete was very patient, but insisted that we practised until we got it right, which we eventually did.

The helicopter was on loan from the Botswana Defence Force, complete with pilot, Lieutenant-Colonel Paledi. He was a very pleasant and relaxed chap with two keen young assistants in training. I could see how dealing with the unpredictable nature of these animals would be very good experience for them.

We spotted the helicopter before the giraffe herd. Giraffes running has got to be one of the most amazing sights I have ever seen. All we could see were their necks rocking forwards and back in slow motion as they galloped along the horizon about a mile away. Even though they look like they are moving slowly, they rocket along at a tremendous pace. Within ten minutes a suitable animal was darted from the helicopter and the ground team leapt into action. I thought we had been driving fast before but Spud, our driver, set off at greyhound pace. I have no idea how we suddenly found ourselves driving next to the giraffe, because I was hanging on so tight and trying to guide Spud round holes in the ground. When I did look up, the giraffe was about twenty metres away, moving gracefully at a canter. They are incredible creatures when standing still, but seeing one run so clearly was a very moving experience. So much so, in fact, that I stopped checking for holes. We managed to get ahead of the giraffe and everybody piled off the vehicle, only to jump back on as it changed direction.

Trude: Once we saw the giraffe, it was important that the roping team went on the ground to break it as quickly as possible. The giraffe was sedated, but it would still run until it exhausted itself if it wasn't stopped. The roping team were running as fast as they could, but several times they had to climb back onto the truck, to catch up with the giraffe again. Finally we caught up with it, and it was starting to look really tired. Steve was running fast and eventually the ropes managed to pull it down.

I ran over with the antidote. It was difficult finding a vein in such a muscular neck and as the seconds ticked by I was getting incredibly stressed. In the panic an experienced member of the capture team lent a hand and I felt a great sense of relief when he got the syringe in. The giraffe started to kick, but was not recovering as quickly as it should have been. Pete was worried that not enough of the antidote had gone in. Pete gave it another dose of antidote. It was a tense few moments and I can't begin to describe the relief I felt when the giraffe got to its feet.

Once the animal was successfully in the truck we were ready to start to drive it to the final trailer, which had been specially built for transporting giraffes. It was a very long drive through the bush, and we had to hang on to the outside of the crate, making sure the giraffe was happy. There were a lot of potholes, and there were several times when I thought I was gong to end my

Giraffe

Size: The giraffe is the tallest land animal at up to 6 m tall. They weigh up to 1.5 tonnes. The heart weighs a massive 11 kg, with walls 7 cm thick to push the blood 2.5 m up the neck to the brain.

Life span: Giraffes live for around 25 years (30 years in captivity has been recorded). Predators rarely attack adults, but only 25 per cent of the young make it past 1 year old.

Distribution: Giraffes used to be found all over Africa, wherever there was a suitable food supply. Now they are found south of the Sahara and in east and southern Africa.

Behaviour: Giraffes are reasonably social animals, moving in herds of 7–8 individuals. They can be found in huge numbers together, but this is a reflection of a concentrated food source rather than social bonds.

Diet: Giraffes use their immense height to browse the branches other animals cannot reach from the ground. They are quite selective, and use their long leathery tongues to strip branches of leaves regardless of huge thorns. Giraffe can go for several days without water and can drink up to 38 litres at one time.

days squashed under the metal frame of this truck with the giraffe on top of me.

Steve: Moving the giraffe into the trailer was a tricky job. First, the truck had got stuck in the soft sand. I set about collecting some branches from small trees to be placed under the wheels. One huge branch needed breaking, and my attempts at jumping on it, to break it, would be better edited out of the programme, as I ended up falling on my behind. Second, it took too much time to align the trailers and the giraffe started to get a little jittery.

Trude: Everything was ready to release the giraffe into the trailer. First we had to climb up and remove the blindfold and the cotton wool. Pete had removed the cotton wool on the other side and the giraffe was already starting to become really panicky, waving her neck about, and moving erratically backwards and forwards. For a moment I saw Pete hanging on to her neck, and I thought he would fall off the truck. She backed into the trailer very quickly, and we still hadn't removed the blindfold. From the ground I could see Pete stretching and asking for something to cut the blindfold, and by a miracle he did it.

We closed the door behind the giraffe, and watched her recover, which she did, incredibly quickly. I climbed up to watch her, and was amazed to see that she was accepting Pete touching her head. Pete told me that giraffes tame very quickly. The length of the giraffe's eyelashes was amazing; they are incredibly pretty creatures.

We followed the specially built trailer in our vehicle, while Denis and Dudley were in another vehicle in front, filming the giraffe as they drove. We were all really pleased with the capture and were looking forward to a relaxing drive down to Mokolodi. Little did we know what lay ahead of us. Five minutes later I was snoozing in the back seat when Michael shook me saying there had been an accident. Gillian had been on the radio, saying they had had a head-on collision and I could hear Denis screaming in the background.

▼ The roping team in action.

Steve: We arrived in a few minutes to be confronted by a mêlée of people and smashed vehicles. The first vehicle had had a head-on collision with another large 4x4 on a blind corner. Their vehicles had got stuck in ruts and had smashed their right wings together.

Denis was still in the vehicle surrounded by people, and it was hard not to fear the worst. He had been holding the camera and was thrown forwards, jamming his arm into the handle. He had broken his arm quite badly, but was otherwise unhurt. Thankfully, there was a doctor with the people who they had run into, and she had straightened Denis's arm and splinted it to a plank. I'm not sure I could have done it if she hadn't been there as, according to Gillian, he had screamed throughout. She had also given him a painkilling injection, but he really needed morphine. I was put in charge of looking after Denis and everybody else set about sorting out transport. We moved Denis into the front of the Land Rover and Andres took over the driving, with Trude and myself in the back.

▲ Transporting the giraffe to the trailer which would take it to its new home at Molokodi Game Reserve.

Gillian and Matias had gone ahead in the Toyota to try and get a helicopter from Gabarone. Andres then told us that we had little fuel left and the Toyota had less, with five hours' drive in the dark ahead of us. Michael and Dudley stayed with the crashed vehicle to sort out the gear as we crept off at a snail's pace. Andres really came into his own, driving as smoothly as was humanly possible, but the roads were very bad.

We made good progress, without jarring Denis too badly. Over a couple of bumps he squealed and sweat poured down his face. We couldn't help anticipating the pain along with him, flinching at every pot-hole – and there were many. We were desperately low on fuel, despite buying some from a French couple who were camped by the side of the road, so we were expecting to find Matias and Gillian stranded at any point. It took us about an hour before we came to a town, where they had found a phone and contacted the medical rescue services. Someone rang back quickly to tell us that the same helicopter that had been with us earlier that day was returning to pick Denis up and would be with us in about half an hour.

Gillian still seemed very agitated despite this excellent news, and I told her to relax as Denis would be fine. She then told me that the doctor had told her that the blood supply to Denis's hand had been compromised, and that if we didn't get him to a hospital soon it would have to be amputated. This was news to me. I walked back to see Denis, and told him I was going to have a look at his hand. I tried to be as calm as possible. His fingers were colder than his other hand and slightly darker. I took a pen and asked him whether he could feel me touching his fingers. He felt them all, and could even move them slightly, which told me what I needed to know. I went back to Gillian and told her that he was going to be fine, explaining what I'd done. At the news, she seemed to deflate, sinking down to the ground against a wall. I couldn't believe that she and Matias had been driving around with no fuel and no communications thinking that Denis was going to lose his hand.

Trude: Andres and I had to find petrol and cars to light up a football pitch for the helicopter to land on. We located the chief of the village in a pub. He was very drunk, and so were the rest of the village, it seemed. We rushed around with the drunk chief in the front seat to find out who could help us with petrol and cars. There were four cars in the entire village, and we managed to wake up the owners and drag them down to the football pitch. Outside, the sky was full of stars, and we could find our way around by moonlight. I felt very tired, and Denis was starting to look really bad.

Steve: They returned with some very drunk, and largely useless, volunteers, and by the time we could hear the helicopter, we only had one other vehicle, so Matias had to stand there with a torch as a substitute. The spotlight from the helicopter blazed down onto the ground as it made its final approach. For a moment, I think Matias thought he was being abducted by aliens, and only just managed to get clear – the pilot seemed to have picked him as an ideal landing spot. All we could see through the dust was Matias's torch waving madly as he ran for it. Afterwards, he told us he had no idea which way to run, so he could easily have run under the helicopter.

Gillian and I were instructed to go with Denis to sort him out at the hospital. I was happy with this, as the alternative was to stay out in the middle of nowhere, with no fuel, surrounded by a huge crowd of drunk people who had just had a helicopter land in their back garden.

The paramedics waiting at the airport ran forward and made to grab Denis by the arm. Some wrist slapping did the trick, allowing us to ease him gently into the smallest ambulance I have ever seen. I kept expecting Sooty and Sweep to pop up in doctors' uniforms. Thankfully it was only a few minutes before we got to the hospital. The on-call doctor was very gentle and thorough, removing part of the splint to check the extent of the damage. He sent Denis for an X-ray and called the orthopaedic surgeon. The X-rays came back and the consultant let me see them after I explained I was a vet. Denis had fractured his radius and ulna, which are the two bones of the forearm, half-way along their length. He had also fractured the radius nearer his wrist which, according to the consultant, was going to be harder to fix. I went back to Denis and explained what he had done and how the doctors were going to attempt to correct it. It was like speaking to a client about their pet's broken leg, and I found myself going into a routine spiel. As he rolled off on his trolley to theatre, Gillian and I ground to a halt. We were exhausted. I walked into my hotel room and fell into bed. It was 1.30 am and I couldn't help thinking of where the others were and wondering whether they would get back tonight.

Trude: We were left behind, and we still didn't have enough petrol to get us to Gabarone. After an hour we met Puso's truck. He said Michael and Dudley were in the next village. We met them and filled up with petrol. Everyone at this stage was dangerously tired. I was very worried about driving – my vision was blurred – and Andres was getting really tired now too. We had to follow Puso's truck and find the giraffe-truck. We spotted them where they had stopped because of power lines hanging across the road. The trailer was too tall to pass underneath them, and if they tried they would risk electrocuting the giraffe. So we had to help to light up the phone cables crossing the road. Then they could lift them above the trailer. It was a lengthy process, and at 3.00 am we were all fighting sleepiness.

Finally we left them and rushed to a hotel. We got lost a couple of times, but when we finally arrived at 5.00 am I had the best

▲ A dream come true for Steve.

▶ The cheetah didn't take kindly to having their dinner taken away.

shower I've had in my whole life. I have never been so dirty, cold and tired.

Day three

Steve: I got up at 11.00 am, but I was still completely shattered. We all went to see Denis in the hospital. He was looking fine and was already a hit with the nurses. He had his arm in a cast but his hand looked very swollen and sore. He had a television in his room and had seen Trude and I in *Vets' School* on the national station this morning, which we laughed about.

Lunch was at Mokolodi Game Reserve. Mokolodi is a small nature reserve set up as an education centre for local people. Puso made use of Trude and I to talk to some local children – when we arrived at the education centre we were faced with teaching the children about a 6-metre python.

Trude: Our next stop was the holding pen where the giraffe we had brought in were being kept. Here they get used to their surroundings before they are released. Already they were showing signs of settling in. It was great to see them, especially as catching ours had been such a nightmare.

Steve: Puso also wanted us to check out his 'cats'. His cats just happen to be two orphaned male cheetahs. Their mother was shot by a farmer because she was killing his goats. After she was shot, the cubs were found mewing in the bushes with their eyes still closed. The farmer's wife reared the cubs until they were too big to handle, and then asked Puso to take them. They have no hunting skills and are too tame to be released, so he built an enclosure for them in the park.

Trude: When we walked into the enclosure the first time, all we could hear was very loud purring. They walked straight over to us, and it was then that I realized Steve was in love with a cheetah.

Steve: I am a cat person anyway, but these two were incredible. Once we relaxed, they were all over us. They licked my face and

neck just like Useless, my cat at home. Their tongues were very abrasive, and I could feel my tan disappearing with every stroke. They are so beautiful and gentle. Unlike the other big cats, cheetahs are very easily tamed and trustworthy. It was like a dream come true for me to be rolling around on the ground playing with such stunning creatures.

We moved them to a bigger enclosure today. Puso had brought their dinner, big joints of bone with sparse flesh on them. Trude and I were given the meat to lure them into the back of a vehicle. I was tall enough to keep the meat out of reach as they sprang to grasp it out of my hands and with a bit of coaxing we had one loaded. Trude had lost her morsel straight away, and now we had to get it back so that we could get the other cheetah loaded. During a brief scrap over the meat both Puso and one of the rangers got caught quite badly with one of the cheetah's dew-claws. Even though the cheetah wasn't really being aggressive, it made it clear that they need to be treated with respect.

Day four

Trude: Today a hartebeest calf that had been abandoned by its mother was brought into the sanctuary. He was just three days old and was a skinny little guy. We put him in a shady pen, I could tell from his skin that he was very dehydrated. We tried to feed him some milk but he was too stressed to eat and so we decided he needed to be left in peace.

Steve: While Trude was helping with the hartebeest, I got involved with another problem with a different antelope. This one was a little larger. It was a full-grown male kudu that had escaped through the fence some weeks ago and had now returned very emaciated and dehydrated. As I arrived at the scene the first thing that struck me was the immense size of the animal, especially its horns. They were huge, and made it very intimidating. On closer inspection, however, this individual was in a very bad state. Its body condition was very poor, with all its bones clearly visible. It was in most danger from its severe dehydration. Thankfully this was being addressed by one of the rangers who was offering a large bucket of water through the wires of the fence.

If fully fit this animal would have either fled the moment it was approached, or even shown some aggression, but it was obviously too weak. I spent ten minutes feeding it twigs dipped in water to try and get some sustenance into it. It just stood there, with a glazed expression on its face, slowly munching away, oblivious to the activity around it. As quietly and gently as possible, the park staff set about dismantling the fence. Even though the animal was subdued it was imperative that we didn't take any chances, as once the fence was down we were going to be at risk from its rather dangerous-looking horns.

Just as we managed to pop the wire over the tips of its horns, the kudu startled and lunged forward. The ranger holding the bucket was knocked sideways and could have had a more intimate encounter with those huge skewers if the kudu hadn't stumbled to the floor. It recovered quickly and trotted away from its rescuers, seeking comfort in the shade of a tree. It was followed for a few hours just to ensure it was OK and later we heard that it had found water, and was eating some hay that had been provided for it, which was marvellous news.

It was only a short trip to the cheetah's new enclosure, and Trude and I stayed with them for about half an hour to see them settling in. They climbed onto the vehicles to get a good view and relaxed very quickly. We saw a hare running in the grass within the fence, which hopefully will provide them with some exercise. If I could have got away with it I would have sneaked one out and taken it home with me. They are so beautiful. I guess I can come back and visit them for another health visit – any excuse!

Trude: At the end of the day I went to check on the hartebeest calf. Although he had taken a turn for the worse earlier he had now been successfully adopted by one of the ranger's wives who was going to take him home and bottle-feed him every four hours.

Day five

Steve: Today we set off on our journey to the Okabanga Delta. It's a long drive just over 1,100 kilometres but worth the effort. It's an area of outstanding natural beauty and because there is plenty of water there are plenty of animals. When we got to Maun we met up with Mike Penman who would be providing a camp for us and the crew while we were in the delta. He is quite a relaxed chap, with hair coming from everywhere. Emerging from the doormat on his chest was a small monkey with a cropped tail, called Fidget. It was into everything. Mike had bought it from some soldiers who had killed its mother and kept the baby to sell. He knew that

buying it would only promote further monkey abuse, but he couldn't leave the little guy there, and I could see why.

Steve: Before heading on for the final part of the journey we had lunch at the Power Station, a very funky restaurant and craft centre. The site is the half-finished structure of what must be one of the biggest cons in the world. Allegedly, a man once convinced the government that he could generate electricity from sand and claimed millions of dollars in grants before absconding, leaving his project incomplete. I think it shows a great sense of humour to have left the place standing and named it the Power Station.

Trude: We soon hit the sandy roads that are so characteristic of Botswana. Just five minutes into the drive, the vetmobile got stuck in the sand for the first time. There seems to be a problem with the weight of the vehicle in a situation like this – it tends to sink every time we slow down slightly. We were towed out by the crew Land Rover and thought it would be fine but after that the roads got even more sandy and the next three hours were spent getting stuck again and again. Steve was driving the first bit and Andres took over after a while. Andres drives at top speed, which led to wild laughter for us, attempting to drive after him as he surfed along across the top of the sand. However, just when we all thought that everything was going tickety-boo, we had to cross some water.

Steve: At the water crossings, I was behind the wheel and being filmed. The vetmobile managed really well in the water, especially as we had to do each crossing twice to film it from the inside and outside. On one crossing, we had made it to the other side when there was a nasty crunch and we lost power to the front axle.

Trude: As we started our second crossing we got very stuck. Water was pouring into the vetmobile and we had to wade out to get the winch on. At this stage we realized that there was no way we would be able to get the vehicle through all the water crossings without the full four-wheel drive working. We abandoned it next to a waterhole where two bull elephants were having a nice shower. They were looking at the vehicle with surprise; they probably thought it was a big yellow banana!

We climbed into Mike Penman's vehicle and spent the next two hours watching the amazing scenery floating past. We saw a big pride of lions dozing on a hill, their beautiful, wise eyes watched us as we drove past. Some of them were rolled over on their backs in the long yellow grass, just like domestic cats. It's strange how quickly you become accustomed to seeing these animals and also how little fear you have of them.

Sitting in my tent, watching the black sky and listening to the bullfrogs, my mind went back to England and Norway. It will be difficult to go back to dealing with hamsters and dogs, and cats with neurotic problems after this. I fell asleep after having checked my sleeping bag for pythons and scorpions. I woke up a couple of times, hearing something sniffing my tent. I also heard the lions roar in the dark night and baboons screaming. There were lion tracks outside the tent the next morning.

▲ Steve's solitary musing in a baobab tree was quickly disturbed by Andres and his camera.
▼ A moment of light relief during a stressful time in Botswana.

Day six

Trude: I woke up to see the sun rise above the water. One of the camp staff asked what we were doing here and I explained. It was strange that he didn't know what a vet was. It made me realize how little education the locals have, and how different my world is compared to theirs. It was really nice to speak to him. We don't get the chance to talk to local people often as they are usually the staff and are busy working. It bothered me a bit in the beginning; I didn't like the fact that the whites are the bosses and the black locals work for them. I know it's more complicated than that, but you can't help feeling strange about the situation. After I explained that I was an animal doctor, he asked if I had some information about the animals. That seemed ironic, as you assume local people will know

more about these animals because they live here, but that is not the case at all.

Did you know?

Giraffes have 7 bones in their neck, the same number as other mammals. These vertebrae are very elongated, with highly developed joints.

Steve: Today we met up with two South African lion researchers called Christian and Hanlie Winterbach. The lions they had been tracking were only a couple of hundred metres from where we had left the vetmobile last night. It was a pride of about twenty-two lions and Christian and Hanlie are following their movements, along with the movements of other prides in the area, to get a better understanding of the population dynamics of this species. We got some great footage of the lions and Christian and Hanlie were really chatty and friendly, coping very well with the cameras. Fidget the monkey was putting on a very defiant face to the lions, from the safety of the vehicle. He kept running down the bonnet and chirping away at them from the safety of the vehicle. The lions were obviously interested in him and we were concerned that Fidget was dicing with death. When the vehicle's engine started and the lions rose to walk away, Fidget did a little stamping victory dance, claiming the retreat to be all his work, much to our amusement.

Trude and I had a bit of a shaving-foam scrap whilst driving along in the vetmobile. Dudley confiscated the foam, and when we had parked up he slipped round the back and wrote 'Just Married' on the door. Trude and I posed for some ridiculous photos with this as a backdrop.

Our new camp is next to water, and I'm starting to get the feeling that there isn't an ugly place to stop in the whole of this area. Christian and Hanlie came for dinner and were great company. On the way to my bed, I took a little time to stare at the stars from the open-topped toilet tent. There is hardly any light pollution here and the sky is a sea of lights. The Milky Way is like a cloud, so thick with stars that it looks like sparkling dust. There is no more humbling experience than to see just how vast an expanse lies out there undiscovered, which mirrors perfectly my view of this continent.

Day seven

Steve: I could have done with a lie-in this morning, as I have been having some very strange dreams since starting the antimalarials. It wasn't a hard start to the day though, as I got to spend a couple of hours writing my diary. The spot I picked for my inspiration was half-way up a baobab tree, close to camp. Baobabs are incredible trees, more like stone than something organic. The swollen pink limbs made for a comfortable seat, and must have looked impressive, as I had only been up there for a few minutes before Andres appeared, snapping away.

The rest of the team were relaxing or packing vehicles before the gruelling day's travelling we had ahead as we headed back to Gabarone. Michael asked me to drive the Toyota this morning. I was hungry to give the sand another try. The Toyota was loaded to the hilt with gear, leaving only the passenger seat spare, which Dudley occupied. We passed the bumpy time chatting away about life and tax, both very complicated subjects – more so tax than life. We made good time through both sand and water, despite the increase in depth of many of the crossings. After collecting the vetmobile we still had a few water crossings to go. We were doing really well and then when we were almost out of the worst areas we got thoughly stuck in deep mud as we tried to cross a shallow river.

Trude: This was the first time I had seen Steve get annoyed. We were in so deep in the mud and the vetmobile was so heavy that the crew vehicle was unable to pull us out so we had to try ourselves with the help of a tree and the winch on the vehicle. Unfortunately the tree was off to one side and because of the angle, and because the winch was not strong enough, we were unable to free ourselves.

Steve: Just when I was ready to torch the vetmobile where it stood, help came from an unexpected quarter. A group of locals suddenly appeared, singing as they walked out of the bush. They were obviously amused by our predicament. The head of this band seemed to be a middle-aged chap wearing a Hawaiian shirt and a cloth cap more appropriate for Dorset than Africa. He set about organizing the women with him to fetch wood, and helped me jack up the back wheels of the vetmobile. When I say helped, I mean he stood there laughing at my attempts. More moral than physical support, but it did put me in a much better mood. He then engaged himself in removing all the mud from under the wheels and placing the wood in its place. With some assistance from a passing vehicle, we had the vetmobile on dry land once more. We thanked and tipped our saviours and they left as they had arrived, smiling and singing.

Trude: It was such a beautiful day, and we were all so happy and jolly when we set off again. I was driving, Steve was sitting in the passenger's seat and Michael and Gillian were in the back seat. As we had quite a long drive in front of us before the next stop, we were singing and making jokes; the atmosphere was really nice. We drove along a dirty, sand road, and the darkness was coming on quickly. Steve and Gillian were singing old hits from the seventies and exchanging favourite songs. I can't sing at all! I was thinking about a film I had seen, where all the people in the car were happy and singing and then they crashed and died and that was the end of the film.

As it began to get dark it was becoming more and more difficult to see the car in the front because of the dust clouds. I kept on slowing down, to give the dust a chance to settle. The road had quite a lot of sand on it, but that was OK as long as I kept to the tracks that had been made by other traffic. The only problem was that these tracks were in the middle of the road.

We had not seen any other cars for a long time, when I spotted two vehicles parked alongside the road. As we approached them, I became concerned that I was too close, and decided to give them a bit more space when passing. I slowed down, and tried to steer the vehicle a bit to the other side of the road, away from the parked vehicles.

As I did that, I could suddenly feel that we had started to slide on the sandbank that I was trying to cross and, to my horror, we started to slide sideways towards the parked vehicles.

Steve: Everything happened in slow motion, as it always does in these cases. Eventually the back wheels gripped the bank and sent us diagonally across the road, directly towards the two cars. Trude didn't brake, which would have been horrific, but swerved violently to the left. We were going to miss the other vehicles, but we were still travelling at some speed and were out of control. As the back end came round for the final time, it built up a wall of sand against the tyres and then the world tipped. Surprisingly, nobody had issued a single sound as the whole thing happened, except for me saying, 'Here we go,' as we started the roll.

As the ground came towards my window I tried to shift my weight into the centre of the cab but my seat belt held me fast. I felt my elbow hit the window as it exploded on the ground. Next I was supporting my weight upside down on the cab roof, feeling it ripple and crunch under my fingers, before we came crashing down on Trude's side. Matias and Dudley, in the Toyota, were right behind us and had seen the whole thing. Dudley's voice filled the cab as he radioed the Land Rover ahead, 'Andres, stop! They've rolled!' This broke our silence and Michael shouted, 'Everybody out!' as he dived forward to clamber out of the front, over the windscreen that was now on mine and Trude's laps. 'Wait!' I said, 'Take your time,' and I threw the windscreen out. I was worried that if people stormed out they would worsen any injuries. I asked if everyone was alright. Trude and Michael said they were OK, but Gillian still hadn't spoken. I asked her, 'Gillian are you OK?' 'Get your foot off me Michael,' was her reply, in a tone that suggested she was more irritated than hurt. It took a few more, less polite requests before it registered with Michael that he shouldn't really be standing on Gillian.

Trude: We were all alive and fine, and climbed out of the window. Steve helped me out. He had blood gushing from a cut on his elbow. I had been cut on the elbow as well, but not as badly as Steve. I was now going into shock, and could not stop crying. I kept on thinking that we could have been killed. Then, when I realized we were all fine, I couldn't stop crying from looking at the total wreck lying on the side of the road. I had wrecked the vetmobile, and almost killed us all in the process. Michael tried to tell me it wasn't my fault and that we were fine, but I wouldn't have any of it. The same accident might have happened with any of us driving, but I suppose I felt so awful because I knew I hadn't had as much experience driving a big vehicle like this as the other members on the team.

Steve: After I had dressed my elbow, Michael asked me to look at Trude's right elbow as she seemed to have cut herself in a similar way. It was a short, deep laceration that was easily dealt with. She was still very upset and shaken up by it all. The people from the parked cars told us there was a nurse station a few kilometres up the road and Andres, Michael, Trude and I climbed into the Land Rover to drive up there.

The freshly awoken nurse was less than gentle with my wound, but she was very professional. I was willing to accept the pain as long as she did a thorough job, even though the iodine being dragged across my bare flesh caused a brief bout of nausea that forced me to sit down. I recovered quickly and even managed to conjure a smile from her when I explained that I was a vet, and was more used to dealing out the painful treatments at this time of night. She said we needed reassessment at a hospital, either at Maun or Gabarone. By the time we returned to the crash site, the others had righted the vetmobile and recovered the spilled contents, including my sunglasses, which had escaped damage better than I had. The cab on the driver's side was crushed right down, making us feel relieved Trude isn't taller. Andres had arranged for a chap to watch the vehicle and he arrived on a horse, drunk as a skunk, and proceeded to make such a nuisance of himself that we eventually tipped him just to go away. I did a piece to camera about 'leaving a part of me in Africa', while pointing out my bloodstains on the yellow paintwork. Matias then drove the vetmobile to a checkpoint we had passed on the way to the nurse station, and we abandoned it.

Trude: Then we headed back to Maun. It was a strange and quiet drive. Andres was driving, and driving slowly. I suppose we were all a bit traumatized by what had happened, and we weren't taking any more risks.

Steve: At Maun we headed straight to the hospital and found a nurse. I asked Michael why he wasn't filming and he looked at me in sheer amazement, shortly before running to get the small DVC camera.

Trude: I was the first one to be stitched, and I was pathetic. When I saw the needle the doctor wanted to use to put the local anaesthetic in, I flinched. It was a cow-sized needle! That was enough to get me really anxious. I am really bad with needles when they are being used on me. As I was sitting there, head down, with my elbow on the table, Steve tried to encourage me. I started to hyperventilate, and thought I was going to be sick. I only had three stitches! I am such a wimp.

Steve: I was up next and knew I was going to require a bit more work. I had to lie down on the table to allow enough access to the wound, which meant I couldn't see what was going on. The cleaning hurt like nothing else, but was mercifully brief. Next came the local anaesthetic, which burned like fire in what was already a tender spot. The numbness spread blissfully over the whole area quickly, enabling me to relax. The male nurse trimmed the ragged edges of the wound and I could hear the characteristic crunching sound of scissors on skin. That was the worst part, especially as at one end of the wound the anaesthetic hadn't fully worked and I felt a momentary stab of pain as the nurse snipped the last piece away. When he had finished, there were eleven tight stitches in a 'V' shape. It was 1.00 am, over five hours since the accident, so after bandaging I was ready for some food and a bed – and thankfully got both.

Trude: The others had some food with Mike, but I just couldn't get rid of the guilty feeling and found it impossible to relax about the accident. Everyone else seem to be back to normal and were joking about it already. I suppose that helped me to recover from the shock more quickly, but at the time, I couldn't see the funny side of anything. As far as I was concerned, I had killed our vetmobile.

Day seven

Trude: Today was a strange day, as we were all trying to recover from yesterday. I rang my mum, and changed my bandage. My elbow was really sore throughout the whole day. I had a long chat with Steve, which really helped a lot. We talked about the accident, and it became easier to see why it had happened. It made me feel less guilty. Steve told me he had crashed cars himself; that's why he was cool about it last night.

After a couple of relaxing hours next to the pool, I had to go to the police station with Michael to report the accident. It took ages before the person we were there to see spoke to us. It was weird to be ignored in that way; it was almost as though he was demonstrating that he would not hurry up for us. It was obvious that he wanted me to say that I had been driving too fast. I thought I was going to end up in jail overnight, but after an exchange of money, I was allowed to go back to the hotel.

Steve: Michael has arranged for us to return to England tonight. All my Shona sculptures are broken, but I am too tired to care. I just want to climb into my own bed and stay there for a few days. It has been one hell of an adventure and we have coped with numerous perils and tragedies over the last few weeks. Now it's back to Lancashire and cattle, sheep, dogs and cats for a short break, while we all recover from our injuries before returning to Africa. I'm actually really looking forward to being home for a while.

CHAPTER 4

Kenya

Day one

Steve: We touched down in Nairobi after a ten-hour flight. It was already 30°C outside, and promised to get hotter. We still had an hour's flight to Mombasa and a ferry ride after that. Matias joined us at Nairobi, looking very bronzed and chilled as usual, and Andres was waiting for us at Mombasa. The drive to the ferry only took about forty minutes because Clement, our driver, was keeping us entertained with his ability to overtake everything in our path, on both sides, regardless of oncoming vehicles, bicycles and pedestrians.

The ferry system was a whole new experience. The loading was supervised by two men in grey uniforms with table-tennis bats in their hands, but they seemed to be there mainly for decoration, because cars were crossing from left to right and back again without any pattern at all. Somehow they all squeezed on and no space was spared. When we arrived on the the other side of the river, I foolishly expected that the people would disembark first but it was a mêlée of vehicles and pedestrians together. Again, miraculously there appeared to be no fatalities, although Gillian mentioned that a ferry had sunk quite recently, and inevitably, given the overcrowding, there had been some deaths.

Trude: When we finally arrived at the hotel in Diani Beach, I just couldn't believe how beautiful the beach was. We left the UK in the rain, and today we were standing on this white beach on the Indian Ocean. Both Steve and I walked onto the beach after having changed into something less hot than black trousers. I thought this was paradise. Well, it could have been, if it hadn't been for all the people trying to sell you things. We had only been on the beach for thirty seconds when we were approached by someone trying to sell Steve drugs. You couldn't just sit there; someone would come over and pester you with something they wanted to sell.

Later I saw some fantastic-looking Masai warriors walking along the beach with white women. I was told that the Masai were male prostitutes. They were absolutely stunning. They had bright red robes and their hair was plaited and dyed an orange colour.

Steve: Dinner was at a neighbouring hotel recommended by Andres. We were joined by Moshin Likoniwala, the local vet who

▲ Taking a leisurely stroll along the seemingly idyllic Diani Beach.

we are going to be working with, and Julie Anderson, a Scottish zoologist, who is the project manager for the Colobus Trust. The Trust was set up to try to protect the colobus monkeys in this area, because their numbers are in huge decline as a result of tourism. They are folivarous (a word we learned tonight), which means that their diet mainly consists of leaves, flowers and unripe fruit. They are also arboreal (yes, another new word), which means they spend most of their time in the treetops. This lifestyle is rather upset by the road that splits their habitat in two.

Colobus deaths on the road are a huge problem because, unlike baboons, they are very uncomfortable on the ground, and tend to dash across open spaces. To combat this, the Trust has been erecting arboreal bridges to allow the colobus to cross at tree height, thus escaping the traffic. Julie explained that the project was also trying to persuade the hotels to limit expansion in areas of forest habituated by the colobus, and that they were hoping to complete a survey of colobus numbers along the south coast of Kenya.

Another aspect of the Trust's work is to help the hotels deal with primate pests, mainly baboons. The baboon population is increasing at three times the natural rate in this area because of the ready supply of food from rubbish sites and tourists. Julie wants to vasectomize all the dominant males in the area, to limit the growth rate. She has enlisted the help of Moshin, who works

Colobus monkey

Size: These very distinctive black-and-white monkeys can weigh up to 14 kg and grow to 60 cm in height

Life span: Predators are not numerous, and colobus can live as long as 20 years in captivity.

Distribution: They are found in the forests of central and eastern Africa, although their habitat is falling prey to tourism on the coast and agriculture inland.

Behaviour: Colobus spend almost their entire time in the tops of trees, sometimes up to 45 m high. A strong male will often defend the group, but there doesn't appear to be any fixed hierarchy.

Diet: Colobus have highly specialized digestive systems to enable them to feed on leaves and unripe fruits. This diet would be toxic to many other animals. An adult can eat 11–14 kg of leaves daily.

locally as a private vet, and gives his services free of charge to the Trust. I am supposed to be assisting with the operation tomorrow, and we discussed it over dinner – it will be the first primate operation for both of us, so it could prove interesting.

The only hitch in the evening was trusting Andres with food. The bar snacks that he assured me were fried coconut turned out to be pork scratchings. The taste was still as nasty after sixteen years of vegetarianism. He took great pleasure from his 'mistake', and I am sure over the next few weeks I will do the same when I work out how to get him back.

Day two

Steve: We met Moshin at his surgery first thing this morning. It is a small, thatched, concrete-walled building with very little space. The main room doubles as a consultation room and operating theatre. The shelves are very bare and the ceiling is marked with numerous damp patches. Veterinary work isn't exactly glamorous over here, mainly because local people are not willing to spend money on pets. Moshin's main client base is the expat community, who have a much more sentimental relationship with their animals. One such lady's dog was due for an operation this morning.

Did you know?

The name 'colobus' comes from the Greek for 'mutilated', as the monkeys have only very rudimentary thumbs.

Trude: I was going to give Moshin a hand with a dog called Dusty. Dusty was a scruffy little mongrel with a bad eye that needed to be removed. Moshin's surgery was very basic compared with the facilities I am used to in the UK. He had the basic drugs available, a reusable drip bottle hanging from the ceiling, no water in the taps and some injectable anaesthetics that I think we used to use about twenty years ago in the UK.

Outside were the most amazing trees, with monkeys hanging from the branches. After struggling to get some water to scrub up with, and spending some time injecting the anaesthetic into the dog's vein, we were ready to rock 'n' roll. I was assisting, and Moshin was cutting. The basic operation was the same as at home, although I would question the sterility of the surroundings, but then again I am used to working in extremely sterile conditions. Steve, on the other hand, is more used to working with large animals, and he thought the surgery was OK. The operation went fine, and I had a nice chat with Moshin. After the last stitch, we let Dusty wake up, although it was an hour before she even

▲ Trude and Steve with Julie Anderson, the Scottish zoologist running the Colobus Trust.

started to move, as the anaesthetic makes the animals sleep heavily for quite a while.

Steve: Michael is keen to include the vetmobile in the programme as much as possible, so he convinced Moshin to scrub up in its sink. Unfortunately the water tank was empty, and all we got was a few pathetic dribbles. Andres and I, motivated by a rather steely glare from Michael, set about trying to rectify the situation. Getting the water was easy, as there are guys travelling about with home-made wheelbarrows, selling water in plastic barrels. Putting the water in the tank was a different story. We didn't have the key for the cap, so as quietly as we could, in order not to disturb the filming, we eased it off using a screwdriver. By the time the operation was finished, the tank was full and you would never have known we had been there.

Moshin's next procedure was the baboon vasectomy. We all drove over to the Colobus Trust house where our patient was waiting. The baboon had been trapped in a wire cage and transported back yesterday. He isn't an alpha male (a top male in the baboon troop), but is very popular with the females – curbing his fertility will hopefully have a profound effect on the reproduction rate of his troop. I was amazed at how quiet he was, considering the activity going on around him. Julie admitted he was very laid-back for a baboon, which might explain his success with the ladies. The trap doubled as a crush cage, which enabled us to squeeze him up against one side and inject him through the bars. Moshin used ketamine, which when given to humans can cause quite nasty nightmares, so we weren't surprised to see the baboon flinching and twitching throughout the anaesthetic. I was struck with just how human he looked. It is very strange to be presented with an animal with hands, and because the anatomy is so human, I felt a little strange when I shaved the surgical site. I operated on one side, and then Moshin did the other. The surgery was very simple and went without a hitch. Once I started, it was like operating on any other animal, and although we could have been quicker, the end result was neat.

Trude: It was Steve's turn to do some surgery now, so I was the veterinary nurse. The operation site was scrubbed and soon the boys were ready for action. There were some colobus monkeys watching from the tree branches above, crossing their legs. As a reaction to the anaesthetic, the 'gentleman' baboon was moving his jaw as if he was yawning, his fingers kept hold around mine and he was moving his arms about a bit.

Moshin had only vasectomized one baboon before, and Steve had only done rams. They were doing fine though, and soon they carefully put the last stitches in. The problem with baboon wounds is that the animals can pick the stitches out – they have the fingers and nails to do it – so Steve tried to use buried stitches. Steve confirmed under a microscope that he had removed the right part, and then the gentleman was allowed to wake up. After an hour or so, he started to move about, and soon he had fully recovered. He was ready to go back to the troop, and next time he is romantic with the females, they won't become pregnant. So, it was all fun and no responsibilities lying ahead for this baboon. He was only the second to be vasectomized in the locality. Soon, more will end up the same way in an attempt to try to control the baboon population.

▲ Above: The 'gentleman' baboon looking relaxed as he awaits his vasectomy.
▼ Below: Trude acting as veterinary nurse to Steve as he undertakes his first operation on a primate.

Steve: The afternoon was spent at a monkey sanctuary run by a Mancunian expat called Sharon. She never misses an episode of *Coronation Street* on satellite, and hasn't lost any of her accent. The sanctuary takes in injured vervet and sykes monkeys from around the area. Unfortunately there is a high incidence of monkey abuse in the region, as the locals try to scare them away. A popular idea is to render a monkey frightening to the rest of the troop by tying pieces of metal around its neck and painting it with bright colours. This causes horrific stress and pain to the particular animal, and doesn't scare the other monkeys at all; on the contrary, it causes the afflicted monkey to be persecuted by the others. Moshin and the Trust recapture these animals and treat them for their injuries before passing them to Sharon.

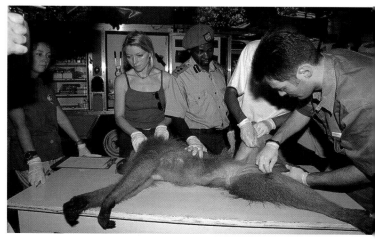

▲ Helping out at ground level with the arboreal bridge.

The monkeys are kept in a large cage, full of interesting things to play with, for three months, so they have time to recover completely. There is a local troop of monkeys that call every day to feed by the cage. The caged monkeys can therefore socialize with the wild troop over a long period, prior to joining them when they are released. This practice works very well, and the wild troop is now almost entirely made up of Sharon's rehabilitated monkeys. All the monkeys have names, and Sharon's love of *Coronation Street* is evident when you are introduced to Jack and Vera! Feeding the monkeys felt strange, as tourists are not meant to do it, but it is important that the monkeys associate food with the site, not the people, and it is essential that the troop comes here to help socialize the captured monkeys.

Day three

Trude: Having located the baboon's troop, we set off on the road. We soon saw the baboons and stopped the car. We had the gentleman baboon in one of the other trucks, and so we unloaded him onto the road. Soon the other baboons started to come out of the trees, wondering why we had one of their troop. We were told to be careful, because they can be very protective of their family members. Suddenly this massive male baboon came walking towards us. We had sticks, but I must confess I was really frightened, especially after having seen the gentleman baboon's teeth when he was sleeping – they have enormous canines, and extremely powerful jaws. I was holding the rope that pulled the door open. I pulled the rope, and our baboon ran towards us and then straight into the forest with his troop. Phew!

Did you know?
Baboon males are men of the nineties. They will befriend and care for a female, and even protect her young, despite it not being related to him.

Steve: Next we went to see an arboreal bridge being erected. It was baking hot. and we stood around doing very little. Our assistance in building the bridge was restricted to running across the road with it, before passing it up to the chap in the tree. I'd much rather have been doing something a bit more mentally or physically challenging, but I realized it can't be that way all the time.

After lunch, we toured the hotels looking for some bad monkey action, but the word was obviously out and they were nowhere to be seen. We did see some baboons on a rubbish tip and the colobus made an appearance today, which was good of them, considering they are the main reason we are here. We watched them move slowly from tree to tree without ever coming to the ground. You can understand why the bridges are so important to them, because they are not designed for land travel. They are beautiful creatures, with their very distinctive long black hair and white stripes. They move so gracefully and leisurely from branch to branch without fear or hesitation, despite the dipping, and sometimes snapping, of the branches they are on.

▲ Steve, wishing he was the one at the top of the trees.

Trude: This afternoon we visited Dusty, to see if she was OK. The owner lived next to the Colobus Trust, so we just crossed through some bushes. Dusty's owner was an old woman with bad legs. She could hardly walk, and couldn't hear very well either. Dusty was

Baboon

Size: Yellow baboon males are usually about 20–25 kg in weight, but males have been recorded at around 45 kg. Females are about half the size of the males.

Life span: The life span of this species is around 20–30 years.

Distribution: Yellow baboons can be found throughout sub-Saharan Africa, as they are very adaptable animals.

Behaviour: Baboons move in large troops, spending most of their time foraging on the ground. At night they seek the refuge of tall trees or cliffs.

Diet: They are omnivorous, feeding on leaves, grasses, berries and even some meat, such as fish and small antelope.

▲ Trude looking menacing with her water pistol.

lying on her own little bed in the living room, and snarled when Moshin sat down next to her. She looked a bit dopey, but wanted to come out for a little walk with me and Moshin. The wound looked OK, apart from the blue spray that Moshin had put on to keep the flies away.

At Diani Beach there are too many monkeys, and they can be a nuisance and a danger to the tourists. In the beginning they can be very entertaining, but when they are grabbing sugar cubes out of your hand and showing their teeth, it's no fun any more. I spoke to Julie about what had been done to reduce monkey numbers, and what is being done at the moment. The most humane, but most tedious, way is to make the monkeys associate stealing food from tourists with something bad and unpleasant. This was why Julie showed me the water pistol. The idea was to shoot them with it when they are about to steal. We were talking about this and other methods of getting rid of the problem, when some young teenage boys in the pool recognized me, and started shouting. They were shouting my name, and would not let us film in peace. They had seen *Vets in Practice* on Kenyan television. That's bizarre. I lost my patience and turned around and shot them with my water pistol. They looked really surprised, but it did improve their behaviour.

Day four

Steve: Today was the start of our journey across Kenya. While waiting for the ferry to Mombasa, we were queuing next to some roadworks. It looked as if they were widening the road down to the ferry. There were four blokes using metal spikes and picks, etching away at a rock face about four metres high and fifteen metres long. They looked like prisoners doing hard labour, but as manpower is so cheap over here it is more cost effective to pay someone to work for months rather than use machinery. It highlighted to me just what it is possible to do by hand, given the time and skill.

Mombasa was very busy indeed and we made slow progress. We filmed some driving shots through the town, including the near-death experience of a cyclist moving just in front of us as he tried to negotiate a busy roundabout. The main road leaving Mombasa towards Nairobi was dreadful. There was evidence of some road improvements as we travelled along, but it was left to road users to sort out traffic control for themselves. When the busy traffic, going in both directions, met at a set of roadworks, it was utter chaos. It wasn't uncommon to be passing down the middle of two trucks going the other way, with cars approaching directly ahead. This was all at very low speeds, because of the terrain, but was still very hair-raising at times.

Trude: Tsavo is a very unusual-looking place; the sand is red and dust covers everything. It is also very hot here. We went straight to a lodge where we met Richard Kock, the vet, Ted Goss, the helicopter pilot and Sammy Adanji, the hirola researcher. Richard is another very nice man. Ted is a character whom it would take me too long to describe here. He is very tall and has a very, very posh English accent. He used to be the head warden of Tsavo and has lived in Kenya most of his life. Sammy is quiet, but razor-sharp. He has dedicated most of his life to the very rare hirola antelope.

Steve: Ted is our helicopter pilot for the next few days. He is is loud and outspoken, but open and amicable. While Richard and Sammy went up in a light aircraft to spot the hirola from the air, Ted drove us around, using a hand-held receiver to keep in touch with the others, trying to find the herd in the local vicinity. He thought that Trude and I were actors pretending to be vets. After we explained that we were qualified vets, he went around assuring everybody, 'Don't worry, they are real people.' We had no success tracking a herd but Richard and Sammy had more luck, with four groups spotted, and one certainly close enough to attempt catching tomorrow.

Day five

Steve: What a day. Hirola capture has got to be one of the most frustrating and laborious tasks ever. They are nervous creatures and don't respond well to stress, making darting them very hazardous. To get round this, they are herded into huge nets and wrestled to the ground by hand before giving sedation, if required. The nets are about three metres high and a hundred metres long, and all have to be erected by hand. This was done by the capture team, who are a specialized group of park staff trained in animal capture. They were accompanied by a couple of Kenyan vets, John Wambua and Dennis Mudakha. For the last few years John has been training in game capture under Richard, while Dennis is more of a laboratory specialist who does little in the field. John strikes me as very capable and confident, which makes him ideal to work with. Dennis freely admits he is the first to run, and is only concerned with being faster than everybody else. He is responsible for the laboratory samples that will be taken from the animals we catch.

Trude: This was one of the most tiring capture projects we have worked on here in Africa. We started off once the hirolas had been located by plane. The basic idea was to set up nets which Ted, in the helicopter, would chase the hirolas into. That sounds very easy, and it could be easy if it was done in the right way, straight away. I think.

We reached the site where we were to put up the nets. We are not talking only one net. No, we are talking about twenty long nets, spread out in a 'U' shape. We started to put them up, using poles and trees. All the time I had to keep on removing these strange burry plants which stuck to my socks, my shoes and to the nets. Tsavo seems to be covered with that kind of plant.

After several hours of work, all the nets were up and we were waiting, behind a bush. Soon we heard the helicopter. We waited

▼ Erecting the huge nets that are used in hirola capture.

and waited but nothing happened. We got a message over the radio that the hirolas had got quite near us, but then had veered away. Apparently we were upwind of the hirolas, so they had smelt us.

Steve: John took over the lead and organized the next site. We were all aware of the weak spots in our previous set-ups, and endeavoured not to repeat the same mistakes. Ted played an important role in the placement of the nets, as he could see how things had gone wrong from the air. Morale was up and everybody was chipping in ideas. As the light started to dim we were ready, and Ted set about driving the hirolas in.

▲ Trude with Ted Goss, the helicopter pilot, one of the most memorable characters they met on the trip.

Trude: The poles were decorated with leaves, and all the nets were hidden perfectly. Soon we heard the herd again. I was looking through the branches to try to see them as Ted herded them closer. I had never seen a hirola before, so I was very curious. Then suddenly I heard a squeal, and everyone seemed to be running in one direction shouting, 'Hirola! Hirola!'

Steve: I was in a bush with John, and suddenly he was on his feet and running. I just had time to see one huge female hit a net and crash to the ground, before she sprang up, free from any entanglement, and sped off into the distance. It was a few seconds before we heard the mewing of a trapped animal and the shouts of those restraining it. Two large adults had crashed through our nets, but two young ones had been successfully trapped. They look like deer with soft, short coats and big gentle eyes. They were quite stressed, so were given a mild sedative. Trude got the blood samples, and various measurements and samples were taken for analysis. Unfortunately, the animals were too small to fit radio collars on, but everybody was on a real high anyway, after such a long, hard day. In many ways, it has enabled us to fit in, because we had mucked in with all the work and the success belonged to us all. I am just glad that I won't ever have to do that again. On the drive back to camp we saw a hirola herd standing by the side of the road. Typical.

Did you know?
It is the Mandrill Baboon that has the really colourful bottom.

▲ Steve assisting with the sedation of a young hirola antelope.

Trude: Tonight in the shower a little bird was watching me, and there were millions and millions of stars above and a few lions roaring now and then. A good environment in which to have a shower. We had dinner with Ted and an American called Lusciele. When Ted had drunk a bit he got very jolly and wanted all the girls to give him a goodnight hug!

Day six

Steve: A quieter day today, thankfully. The morning involved driving around camp to get shots of the terrain. The light was beautiful, making the dry grass look like fields of golden corn. As we drove along, we stirred up lots of insects and pretty soon we had hundreds of swifts circling the vehicle, feasting on the wing. It was incredible.

After lunch, we met up with the capture team who had darted a lioness to radio-collar it. Unfortunately, it had crawled into a thicket with another female and her cubs. It had already been anaesthetized for thirty minutes by the time we arrived, and the plan was to flush out the other lioness and the cubs with a vehicle.

The bush was about a hundred metres from the road and we crawled over in a convoy of vehicles. John Wambua was in our vehicle, and we moved round to the far side of the bush. We started filming as we circled the bush. However, all we could see in the background was Andres in his vehicle, its nose aimed at the sky. His back left wheel had fallen in a hole and he was completely stuck. It was hilarious. He couldn't have picked a worse spot in which to get stuck, as he was only about ten metres from the lionesses. Some brave soul managed to tow him out and he got his vehicle out of shot so we could continue.

The lioness and cubs were flushed out of the bush by nudging it with a vehicle and revving the engine. They were very young cubs and really struggled to run away, tripping over feet they hadn't yet grown into. When we were sure all the other lions were gone, we then had to assess how sleepy our lioness was.

Trude: John was being brave. I wanted to stay in the car, but Steve wanted to be out there with John. They did the little stick trick, and concluded that she needed a bit more anaesthetic. John

actually injected her … brave man. She was then pulled out into the open. She was full of fat ticks, and covered with scars. We took blood samples and fitted the radio collar. This was done so that Sammy can track the lions and see if they are eating his hirolas. When we finished, we reversed her and sat in the car waiting for her to wake up. She wobbled a lot, and I think she was hallucinating because of the ketamine we had given her, so she looked really confused and unhappy. Soon she was well enough to wobble back into a bush, where we left her once we were sure she was OK.

Steve: The sun was sinking on the way back and the insects were stirring at our progress again. This time we had carmine bee-eaters flocking around us. They are the most beautifully coloured birds I have ever seen, with bright red wings and an emerald-green head. They swooped and hovered all around our vehicles in huge numbers, catching their meal. I could have watched them all day. I think I'm turning into a bit of a bird spotter!

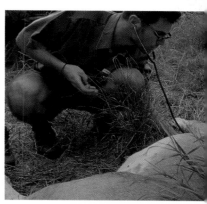

Day seven

Trude: Woke up to a lion's roar, after a night fighting with a giant beetle and some mosquitoes. I am very tired, but can't stop admiring the beautiful view of the riverbank.

Steve: The main task for the day was to radio-collar a recent addition to the park. A large black rhino had been 'misbehaving' – killing two other male rhinos – in another park, and was moved here to see if he would settle down. You'd think they'd realize they're endangered!

After some time the capture team found him, and were ready to attempt a darting. The plan was for John to dart from the helicopter. We were listening to his progress on the radio. The first dart bounced out and the rhino ran away. John wasn't confident the second dart had gone off properly, but the rhino did go down eventually. The ground crew rushed in and Gillian filmed their progress from the helicopter. Andres ran ahead of the rest and ended up nearly face to face with a very irate rhino. Gillian was screaming at him from the chopper, trying to direct him away. She said she was convinced it was going to have him. Ted zoomed back to pick us up and was complaining that he was very low on fuel, as we shot over to where the others were. It was like a scene

▲ Radio-collaring a lion so that Sammy, the hirola expert, can monitor whether the lions are eating the rare antelope.

Putting a radio collar on a badly behaved rhino proves to be heavy work for Steve.

from a Vietnam war movie, the way he dropped down to the ground, kicked us out and took off immediately. We were out and running into the bushes as if the Viet Cong were on our tail. Unfortunately, we had got so disorientated on landing that we ran the wrong way and Ted had to direct us from the air.

The rhino had gone down in a bush at the side of a dry river-bed. He was huge, for a black rhino, and scarred on his head from all the fighting he had been involved in. A chainsaw was brought out to hack away the bushes to enable us to gain access to his head. Radio collars are not used much on rhinos, as they don't have much of a neck to put them round. Sometimes they drill a hole in the horn and place the transmitter directly into it. John had got hold of a specialized collar with an elastic section, a bit like some domestic cat collars.

I helped John fit the collar, which involved lifting the considerable weight of the rhino's head. This type of work is physically hard, even compared with farm-animal work, but I love it. It was very humid and hot in the still air of the riverbed, so pretty soon we were wet through with sweat. Working with John is great, as he really involves us and welcomes suggestions and comments. John got me to give the reversal agent to the anaesthetic, and we all moved to the other side of the riverbed. The rhino was facing away from us but it stood up quickly, turned round and headed in our direction, with some degree of purpose. I knew the rhino would still be a bit dopey so I wasn't too worried, as long as I could keep him in sight. When I did lose sight of him, it was a little worrying and I picked up the pace a little. I got back to the clearing where the cars were parked to find Dennis standing on top of one. The rhino was briefly visible once more, standing beside a bush, with Andres on the other side. He obviously hadn't learnt his lesson. They both shuffled left and right, until the rhino got bored and moved off in the other direction, disappearing in a crash of breaking branches. All we could do was laugh.

Our camp has moved to a fantastic riverside setting. On the way over we filmed lots of driving shots while we had the time. The river was chocolate-brown with mud, but still looked very inviting. Andres was in straight away and I swiftly joined him. It was great just to wash off the grime of the day, and the water was

Did you know?

Lions can go for 5 days without water. They can survive by drinking water from the stomach of their prey. They also get water by licking dew off each other.

as warm as a bath. Dudley managed to find an underwater rock with his belly as he launched himself in, bruising himself quite nastily. There's always one!

Dinner was excellent as usual, and Andres laid on some extra entertainment when I rubbed raw chillies around the rim of his wineglass when he wasn't looking. He was pacing up and down sucking in wind like he was suffocating. It was payback for the pork scratchings incident, but I still felt a little guilty. He forgave me, and just before retiring we walked along the river, looking for game with torches. There were two lions on the other side moaning away, and a large crocodile sailed quietly past where we had been swimming.

Day eight

Steve: We met up with John Wambua and the capture team quite early to try to find another lion to radio-collar for Sammy's research. We drove for miles across the grassy plains looking for lions and eventually one of the vehicles found a pride by a dry river-bed. There were three lionesses with their cubs and one adult male.

Our only problem was a herd of elephants just round the bend in the riverbed. If we started working out of the vehicles and they

Lion

Size: Lions can weigh from 150–230 kg. Males are up to 50 per cent heavier than females. They are usually 2–3 m in length.

Life span: On average a lion will live for 13 years, although they can live for up to 30 years in captivity. The average male life span is half that of the female.

Distribution: There used to be lions in south-eastern Europe, the Middle East and India as well as Africa. Now there is only one non-African population left, in India.

Behaviour: Lions are the only cats to live in social groups (called prides). Prides consist of 3–40 animals, all the females are of the same family, they will suckle each other's young. A pride can have a territory of up to 400 square km, but it is often overlapped by other prides.

Diet: Lions will eat a variety of prey including mice, lizards, tortoises, young elephants, rhinos and hippos. The females catch over 75 per cent of the prey. They have only a 20 per cent kill rate. They kill their prey by covering the muzzle and suffocating them. They also scavenge from hyenas, cheetahs and leopards. Lions can eat 15–30 kg of food at one sitting, and often don't eat for days afterwards.

came to investigate, it could get very dangerous. We decided to attempt to scare them away, using the capture team's vehicle. The herd consisted of between twenty and thirty adults with their young. Our driver drove noisily up to the edge of the riverbank, while all the occupants of the vehicle whistled, shouted and banged the sides of the vehicle. The elephants' first reaction was to accept the challenge and investigate this nuisance, and I was sure we were going to get charged. However, then they slowly moved off, up the other bank and away. One young bull elephant with the group decided that he wouldn't give in so easily. He came up our side of the river and gave us a huge display of mock charges and ear-flapping, before turning and joining the others. He was convincing enough for us all to prefer to retreat quite a distance, though.

A lioness was selected and darted, scaring the pride over to the other side of the river, where they hid under a bush. The next difficulty was trying to get the vehicles across the riverbed to scare the pride farther away. The bank was so steep on the far side that the vehicles couldn't get close enough. I was still with the capture team, who all jumped out of the vehicle and picked up sticks. Not one to be left out, I did the same. I had no idea what they were doing, but went along with it. They walked across the riverbed whistling and shouting and throwing sticks into the bushes. I was utterly amazed at how casual they were about it all, especially as the lions had cubs with them. I was shouting, 'Oi, you cats, get out of my garden!' because that's what it was like – shooing domestic cats.

Lunch was at Voi Lodge, which is on the side of a hill over-looking the vast plains of Tsavo. There was a waterhole at the base of the hill, and we spent our time on the balcony watching young elephants playing. One elephant was chasing storks round and round the pool, with ears flapping, and trumpeting away hilariously.

Day nine

Trude: I tried to drive the vetmobile for the first time since the accident and I was really surprised at how panicky and frightened I felt. I just couldn't do it. Once I started to drive I panicked, and asked Michael if it would be alright for me not to drive. I had never thought I would feel so strongly about driving the vetmobile again. I think losing control of it once made me realize how easy it would be

◀ Another lioness under suspicion of feasting on the hirola.

competition with domestic stock – and is now only found in northern Kenya and some parts of Ethiopia.

Trude: We drove out into the bush to locate the Grevy's zebras. They were very calm when they were watching us. There were mares with foals, and pregnant mares, and they looked more like donkeys than I expected. We drove up to a bigger group with Mount Kenya on the horizon. There are 3000 Grevy's zebras left in north Kenya. There are three protected herds, one of which is here in Lewa. The main threats are poaching and competition for grazing lands with cattle farmers. They were once wanted for their skin, but thankfully there's no market for that now.

Steve: John loaded the gun with the appropriate charge and dart and handed it to me. Ian lined up the vehicle for me to get a shot at one of the big females about seven metres away. I stood out of the hatch in the roof and took aim. I was very nervous because of my unfamiliarity with the gun and the distance involved. The zebra was moving among other animals, and I missed the opportunity. I could tell Ian was worried. He stressed that I should take any chance I got.

▲ A close inspection of a Grevy's zebra reveals the differences between these and the more common Plains zebra.

The next zebra stood even farther away, but I had to try. I aimed and fired quickly. The dart glanced off the rump, exploding its drug load as a mist over the animal's back. I was disappointed that it hadn't stuck, but was relieved that I'd hit the animal. John took the next shot, hitting the neck, perfectly. Ian was keen to catch two, so John loaded again and handed me the gun. I took John's advice to aim for the neck, and was much happier when the dart hit home.

John's animal fell first, and we rushed over to inspect it. The stripes are amazing close up, and we couldn't help stroking them, to see if we could feel the difference between black and white. Various samples were taken including blood and dung for analysis of the zebra's health and parasite burden. Both zebras were lifted into the lorry by hand and given the reversal agent. They came round quickly and stood up. The lorry was perfect for moving these animals. The peat lining the floor gave a good cushioning grip, which allowed them to stand safely. It may have been comfortable for zebra transport but it was very uncomfortable for me. Trude and I sat on the top of the lorry, to keep an eye on the zebras on the way to the boma. The road was very rough and my backside was black and blue by the time we arrived. The zebras were unloaded into the boma, to join some that had been caught before we arrived.

Once another female had been caught, it was decided that there were enough zebras to load up and drive over to their new home. Six females and one male were loaded carefully back into the lorry. We discussed how many it would be safe to transport, considering that we had only had two in the same lorry earlier in the day. It is actually better to pack the animals in, as they are less likely to be thrown around and damage themselves. Once loaded, the next job was to sedate the animals for the journey. This was a little difficult, because as we reached in to inject them,

▼ The Grevy's zebra successfully arrive at the boma in the hills.

we were faced with snapping jaws. It was a matter of stabbing the drug in quickly when you got a clear shot.

The drive involved quite a climb into the hills, and took about six hours in total. Halfway there, the ranger on the back of the lorry signalled that there was a problem. We all leapt out of the vetmobile and climbed up to take a look. One of the animals had fallen down and was looking very stressed. John was naturally concerned. We poured water over it to cool it down and coaxed it back to its feet by poking it with a stick.

Did you know?

There are many theories about why zebras have stripes. The popular ones are that they confuse predators when running together, repel flying parasites and that they help keep the animal cool by causing swirling air currents.

Trude: Five minutes down the road she collapsed again. She was now lying on her side. Things were looking grim, but John decided that there was no point in stopping here. We decided to hurry on to the enclosure.

Steve: After half an hour the ranger gave us the thumbs-up to let us know it had stood up again. The road wound its way up through some spectacular mountain scenery in the mountains. We arrived at the boma on top of a huge plateau just as the sun was setting. The zebras unloaded easily, even the one that had fallen.

Returning in the dark took less time but was more tricky. At one point the convoy got split up and we lost one vehicle. Thankfully we had the radios and lit all the spotlights, so that the lost vehicle could see us. It looked like a scene from *Close Encounters,* but it worked.

Day twelve

Steve: I had some very weird dreams last night, and consequently didn't sleep too well. I'm going to stop taking my antimalarials because I'm sure they are responsible.

Today we met Bimbi, who is the wife of the park manager and also the stand-in veterinary surgeon. She has no formal veterinary training, and picks up the job as she goes along. She lives in the most idyllic house I have ever seen. It is an open-fronted thatched cottage set in the most beautiful garden. There are flowers of every shade and colour decorating her borders, and lovely green grass. Whole tree trunks make up parts of the roof and walls, giving the impression that the house has grown rather than been built. We chatted about various aspects of veterinary medicine, and it is obvious that Bimbi wants to glean as much knowledge from us as possible while we're here.

Trude: Bimbi is a soft touch – you might even say she's an eccentric – when it comes to animals. I was quite surprised when I met Bimbi – I wasn't expecting someone even fairer and smaller than me! Even the hornbills in her garden are given the VIP treatment. Everyday they come to eat in her living room where she keeps a box of mealy worms. She was so full of enthusiasm about everything and we clicked immediately.

Steve: The afternoon was spent water-skiing. High up in the hills there is a small man-made reservoir. Trude wasn't keen to have a go, so it was left to me. I was given a wetsuit without arms or legs, and BBC Safety had supplied us with a life jacket. When opened out, the life jacket could have kept me alive in the mid-Atlantic for about three days, with its distress beacon, full-face hood, whistle and compressed-air canister! It wasn't particularly suitable for water-skiing, however, so after a brief science-fiction piece to camera, I exchanged it for a more modest buoyancy aid. While standing in the water, I felt a sharp pain on my thigh and reached down to see what it was. I was a little surprised when I encountered a leech feeding away. Needless to say, I decided to wait on the shore. I am sure the others expected me to be useless at water-sking from the jibes I got beforehand. Little did everyone know, I'd had a bit of practice last year. I must have been out there for about an hour having a great laugh. I did have some spectacular falls, though, which pleased the crew.

Bimbi came to dinner and brought with her a matchbox of worms that I had asked her for. I only needed to try to find a way to get them into Andres's food. What I didn't know was that, Bimbi had slipped some into my dinner. It was only after I'd polished them off that she told me. Wicked woman! During dessert, I walked up to Andres and patted him on his right shoulder. As he turned round, I tipped the matchbox out onto his cooked banana. He never noticed a thing. He simply chatted to me about how the bananas were best served with a bit of honey and melted butter. I agreed the butter was important, while watching a mealy worm slowly move along the length of the banana he held in his hands. When I returned to my end of the table, we were laughing so much that he got very suspicious, and with rather a sick look on his face asked

Did you know?
Male Grevy's have been reported to kill lions by kicking them.

me what I'd put in his food. Rather than tell him, I tapped the matchbox contents out onto his side plate. He was horrified, and took little consolation from the fact that I had eaten some too. He did laugh about it, and swore to get me back, so I'll have to be on my guard for the next few days. As an encore, Bimbi and I ate a mealy worm each to prove that they are not poisonous. Nobody else seemed keen.

Day thirteen

Steve: This morning was spent game-driving to get some footage of Grevy's zebras. We found them quite easily, and Denis and I really got into the wildlife stalking bit, creeping ever closer and holding back when they looked as if they were going to move off. It was nice to spend some time actually following specific animals, as opposed to filming and moving on. At one point we had common zebras and Grevy's zebras next to each other, so we could really see the differences in anatomy and markings. The other game, including the birds, was excellent this morning, and I really took the time to enjoy it.

We met up with Bimbi later to go and meet Charlie, who, like her, does any veterinary work that needs to be done. He is a quiet chap, especially compared to Bimbi, but very friendly and humorous. He coped very well with the eight attempts to introduce ourselves to him on camera, and we had a very easygoing chat around the table about various surgical and medical problems they have to deal with.

The afternoon's treat was castrating a tom-cat owned by one of the staff in the park. Trude was lined up for the task, leaving me relatively free. We didn't have the same anaesthetic agents available that are commonly used in the UK, so there was a degree of discussion about what would be the best substitute.

Trude: I had anaesthetized the cat and it was laid out on the table. I am normally very confident with my work, but for some reason I felt really intimidated by Steve's presence. Maybe I was worried he was going to criticize me. Steve picked up the vibes, and went off with Bimbi to see some horses. The castration went well. I showed Charlie how to do it – he was eager to learn, and hopefully next time he will be doing it himself.

Steve: Ian's brother and his wife have a small hotel and run horseback safaris. They have about thirty horses, most of which are stabled in a very pretty thatched stable block. The horse we had come to see had a very sore eye that was weeping quite badly. The cornea had gone cloudy fairly quickly, indicating some damage. They thought it had either spiked its eye on a thorn, or had been bitten by an insect on the eye itself. Bimbi had told them to use antibiotic eye ointment. After questioning, they told me that a few horses had come down with similar

signs last year and that one had gone completely blind in one eye. It looked very similar to a condition in sheep and cattle that is caused by bacteria and transmitted by flies. While I was there, they got me to vaccinate all their horses for African horse sickness, and I took this opportunity to look at their eyes. Most of the horses had at least very early signs of the infection, and some even had quite bad lesions that hadn't been seen. This was a nasty outbreak. First, we needed to identify all the horses with lesions, and I showed Bimbi some of the ones with early signs, so she could recognize it in the future. The eye ointment being used wasn't really strong enough, so I gave them a few options and they said they would try and get some for tomorrow. Second, they needed to take preventive measures to reduce the spread of the disease and stop it recurring. This would involve trying to reduce the fly population using repellents, fly-strips and even a change in building design. I was very glad Bimbi had asked me to take a look. It must be a real hassle having to cope with all these problems without the training. I really enjoyed the afternoon, because I had done some very useful work. I would love to spend a year or two here, just working for my keep, especially as the work is so interesting.

▲ Steve, Trude, and Bimbi are introduced to the camels by the lodge manager, Gitonga.

Day fourteen

Did you know?
Camels can close their nostrils to protect them in sandstorms.

Steve: Il Ngwesi is a lodge and group ranch owned and run by the local people. It was the first of its kind and is very successful. The Ndorobo who own the land grouped together to start the project, building a self-catering lodge and running camel-back safaris. The male camels are prone to wandering off in search of females, so Bimbi and Charlie have started castrating them in an attempt to calm them down. So far it has worked very well.

The drive over was very rough but there was plenty to see. While still within the park, we came upon some white rhino that were originally from Kruger. It was great to see that the efforts of the South African team had borne such good fruit. Bimbi was a constant source of information and stories. We prised out her real name, which is Rosalyn. Bimbi is the nickname her African nanny gave her, and means 'nuisance', which suits her much better.

Trude: We went over to the enclosure with the manager, Gitonga. I couldn't believe how tall the camels were. They are obviously well adapted to life in the desert and other dry parts of the world. Their feet are wide, so as not to sink and they have several rows of eye-lashes to protect their eyes from the sand. Gitonga told us that they can bite and kick badly, but he introduced us to a 'nice' one. The way they greet you is to sniff your face for a couple of seconds. I couldn't help feeling nervous about it biting my face. It moved its head very close to my face and sniffed me. I could feel the fine hairs on its muzzle. It must have decided it didn't like me, because it tried to grab my head, but got hold of my hat instead. That was it; I had lost my confidence completely. I decided from then on to treat them the same way as I treat hamsters – with care.

Steve: The handlers got the camels to sit down, which is a huge feat of engineering. The animals were restrained by tying their front feet to their elbows to stop them getting up. The noise they made was like a lion roaring with its head in a bucket of water. The handler then grabbed each camel in turn by the lower lip, and a noose was placed around each one's neck to raise the jugular vein, which was as thick as my arm, making injecting easy. We sedated the camels and waited for them to settle.

Trude: We got ourselves organized for our big castration day: Bimbi and I under one tree, and Steve and Charlie under the other. The plan was to sedate the camels intravenously, then put a local anaesthetic in the skin and in the testicle itself. Then the most bizarre race started. It was the girls against the boys.

Our first camel was a bit tricky. I hadn't done any large-animal work before, so this was as much a learning experience for me as it was for Bimbi. Bimbi had done quite a lot of this work, so I think she just wanted to get some surgical advice. Our patient was a noisy one – I had no idea that camels can make so much ugly noise. It was roaring like a monster and showing off the most disgusting teeth, and had a big green tongue. It kept on waving its neck and head to try to get to Bimbi while she attemped to get the injection in. I was completely stunned. I hadn't expected them to be so aggressive. Once the sedative was in the vein, the camel relaxed. It was lying down, with a rope around one leg to prevent it from getting up.

We now had to prepare the operation site, so we scrubbed the camel's skin as well as we could. The camel was lying in dust, so sterility wasn't going to be perfect.

The skin was very thick to cut. I found it frustrating not to being able to see what I was doing, and was concerned about the dust and soil contaminating the wound. Soon one testicle was out and cut, and I was working on the other. I am not used to working with such big testicles! I have castrated a number of different species, but nothing as big as these.

Steve: The plan had been to do two camels only, but the tribe were keen for us to do more. Two more camels were lined up and we set off as before. We were only halfway through our second camel when the girls came sauntering over, claiming victory in the

Camel

Size: The dromedary (one-humped camel) can grow to about 3 m long, 2.3 m at the shoulder in height and 600–1000 kg in weight.

Life span: Their life expectancy is about 40 years.

Distribution: The dromedary is a domesticated species and can be found in south-west Asia and North and East Africa. There are numerous feral herds found in these areas.

Behaviour: The camel was domesticated between 4000 and 2000 BC. They are renowned for their ability to conserve water. Camels can lower their temperature to 34°C at night, so that they start the day cool, and allow it to rise to 42°C during the day, so they sweat a lot less than other animals. Their dung is so dry it can be burnt straight away.

Diet: Camels eat grasses and leaves. The hump is made of fat and is a food reserve, not a water supply.

▲ Steve and Charlie get on their knees and down to work.

race. We claimed that we were taking our time to refine the technique, but I was amazed at the speed with which they had finished. They were well on with their third camel by the time we were finished with our second, so I went over to indulge in a little espionage. They were both operating at the same time on a testicle each, and from the rear they looked like two little blonde terriers in a feeding frenzy. I had to admire their competitive spirit. They finished in record time, and came to watch us tackle our last patient. Then we all tidied up and agreed that it had been a very successful day.

The tribe were very pleased indeed, and arranged a 'thank you' dance. Bimbi and Charlie explained that it wasn't something they did for tourists, and we were very honoured to see it. I was glad it wasn't filmed, because it was something very personal. The singing was deep and resonant, and the dance was very rhythmical, involving huge leaps in the air. Their timing was excellent. I was telling Bimbi about my basketball leaps, when she shoved me forward and asked whether I could join in. Gatinga, the chief, waved me over. I think I surprised a few of them when I jumped as high as they did, but they had a good laugh at my lack of grace in the air. It was a tremendous privilege, and the best payment I've ever received for veterinary work.

▲ Steve just couldn't resist the opportunity to run at a large flock of birds!

Day fifteen

Steve: We arrived at our hotel in the early evening. We met up with another film crew, who are covering the marabou storks, and William Kimosop the head warden. Dennis Mudakha also arrived, full of smiles as usual. I was sitting next to William's brother, Raphiel, who is a graphic designer. He explained a lot about Kenyan culture and politics to me, and was very interested in English culture and our standard of living. His criticism of his government could have earned him detention and torture until 1992.

Day sixteen

Steve: We set off at 6.00 am on a drive to the lake shore. It only took a few minutes and the light was increasing by the minute. When the road started skirting the lake we had our first impression of the flamingo numbers. William told us that there were around two million on the lake, and I could well believe it. It was the first time I had had any concept of what a million of anything looks like. Most of the birds were around the shoreline, which was one huge, swirling pink mass. The lake is flanked on the east side by ridged mountains that are typical of the Rift Valley. As the sun rose it became apparent that it was going to be a very hot day. Trude and I helped Dennis and his team build their inflatable boat, and then we set off in the vehicles to survey a few sites and assess the state of the flamingos. Dennis explained that we were just trying to estimate the level of lame birds and to see if any of them were sufficiently moribund for us to catch them. The first site was at the north end of the lake. The shore is flat and featureless, and nothing grows in the lake apart from algae, because of the water's high saline and alkaline content. The flamingos, however, have evolved to capitalize on this abundant food source by developing sophisticated mouths that sift the algae from the water. The only reason they are pink is because of the very high pigment content of their diet.

In 1996 and 1997, as many as 50,000 birds died here. The cause was unclear, but was thought to be a combination of stress (it was at a time of severe drought and many feeding areas had dried up), bacterial infections and possibly algal toxins due to excessive mixing of the water from inclement weather. At that time it was possible to catch the birds by hand. The situation today was totally different. To highlight the futility of running at the birds, I suggested we gave it a go as there is something about scaring birds into flight that never leaves you from childhood. Dennis was up for it as he likes a good laugh, so we sprinted full tilt at a group up the shore. Even the lame birds managed to escape from us with ease. The plan was to set some snares to catch some birds, if we couldn't find any sick enough to pounce on. We moved up the shore to check some other sites, and on the way Denis the cameraman spotted a dead bird in a bush and hopped out to film it. As he got close he noticed that it was still alive, so we rushed down to collect it. It was caught in a wait-a-bit bush, and the tiny thorns had lacerated its legs very badly. Dennis was pleased, as this meant we didn't have to set any snares. The bird had got an old injury on one thigh that may have explained how it got caught in the bush. We put it in the vehicle intending to put it to sleep, but it died before we could inject it.

It was approaching midday when we returned to the boat and headed out onto the lake. We cruised around talking about the ecology of the lake and taking water samples. Our second catch of the day was a dead bird floating free in the water, which we kept to post-mortem later. The crew filmed us from the shore moving towards the flamingo and soon we had birds all round us. It was so impressive. The whole air just turned pink.

We shared lunch with some marabou storks. They are enormous birds that look like a cross between a stork and a vulture. They look just like undertakers when they walk, with their wings crossed behind their back, but they are lightning-quick at snapping up food, including weak flamingos.

Dennis and I did a post-mortem on the flamingo we had found in the wait-a-bit bush. Bird anatomy was coming back to me slowly, from barely remembered first-year lectures. Nothing abnormal was found apart from the injury to its thigh, so this was regarded as the cause of death. It was obvious that Dennis and I didn't want to post-mortem the other bird, so I said, tongue in cheek, that it was too decomposed and that it had probably drowned. Dennis thought this was hilarious, but accepted it so we could wrap up for the day.

▲ Trude, Steve and Dennis doing a post-mortem examination on the flamingo they found in a wait-a-bit bush.

Day seventeen

Steve: The last thing we did was to visit one of the large boiling springs. This was a circular pool about five metres in diameter, with the centre boiling away furiously. It looked like it must stop at some point, but it just kept on boiling away, kicking out steam. Occasionally we were bathed in the water vapour, which was like a very hot sauna, especially as the sun was already frying us. We could have done with an ice-cold plunge pool right next to the spring – but you can't have everything, I suppose.

Trude: The boiling springs on the lake are an added bonus for the flamingos. They drink the hot water as well as using the springs to steam-clean themselves to get rid of fleas. I didn't like to imagine falling into the water. instead we boiled some eggs. They were perfect and hadn't gone green like mine usually do – when I cook them for six minutes!

CHAPTER 5

Uganda

Day one

Steve: We were on the road at 7.00 am this morning after a very poor night's sleep. Our destination was the equator.

We reached it in good time. It is marked by a white line across the road and two concrete markers on either side. It was all rather understated, but as the equator crosses right through Uganda, the people must get quite bored by it. We filmed two lads showing us the water-spinning trick – water spins clockwise down a hole in the southern hemisphere and anticlockwise in the northern hemisphere. On the equator it doesn't spin at all, which is the weirdest thing to see.

The rest of day was spent driving right across the country from east to west. It was so green compared to where we'd been. At times I woke up and thought we were back in England, because we were driving through rolling green hills, but then we would come across huge banana plantations. Eventually, we dropped onto a more arid plain where Queen Elizabeth Park is situated. The park lies along the shore of Lake Edward, which is huge. You can't see across it, but it's not a patch on the size of Lake Victoria when you look on a map. The lodge is pretty but unfinished. We all met Ludwig Siefert, the vet we are going to be working with here. He seems very friendly and quite enthusiastic.

On the way to bed I stood under a streetlight and watched the bats spin and turn, making the most of the moths' confusion. I was joined by a nightwatchman, who explained the various types of bat that are native to the area. I love the open, friendly attitude of people here in Uganda.

Day two

Steve: The first job of the day was to catch an orphaned baby warthog. Its mother had been causing havoc in a village just outside the park and was poisoned by the villagers. The piglet was still living in the village, and was probably going to suffer the same fate if it wasn't caught and found a new home. Ludwig had contacted Kampala Zoo, who were willing to take it. Two attempts had been made already, but the wily porky had eluded capture on both occasions.

▲ Margaret, who was quite unlike any of the other vets Steve and Trude met, would prefer to be working with poultry than wildlife as she would make more money to support her family this way.

We arrived at the village and were immediately presented with the burnt carcass of the mother. Ludwig explained that the villagers were Muslim, so didn't kill the warthog for meat. We spent about half an hour unravelling a tatty fishing net to drop on the piglet as we flushed it out of its hole – only to find it wasn't home. We will try again tomorrow.

Ludwig is a lecturer in Uganda's veterinary school, and a number of his ex-students are working with him in the wildlife sector. One of them, Margaret Driciru, is studying lions in the park. There is a problem in Africa of disease transmission between domestic and wild animals. Two diseases they are looking at are FIV (the cat equivalent of HIV) and the distemper virus. Distemper is a disease suffered by dogs that has been crossing over into wild cats such as lions and leopards. The reason for this is thought to involve a mutation in the virus, with hyenas acting as a vehicle for transmission between dogs and the big cats.

Margaret is nothing like the other vets we have worked with. She was dressed in an embroidered denim top and skirt, and a very bright headscarf. No khaki was evident at all. She readily admitted to not liking the work, and said she would prefer a career in the poultry business. This sounded incredible at first, but Margaret has to support a large family of brothers and sisters, and wildlife work is not well paid.

This afternoon we met Dr Christina Wippich Whiteman, a vet from Brazil who is studying how leopards are affected by FIV and distemper. Leopards are solitary creatures and very shy. Ludwig had started setting up a leopard trap near the shore. The trap would have to be manned as, once caught, a leopard needs to be sedated quickly, because they can easily become stressed. Ludwig left us helping to construct the 5-metre metal cage while he went to fetch the bait. I got a little too enthusiastic and managed to erect more of the cage than he had wanted, but he was very laid-back about it all, laughing at my efforts, and we set about erecting it again with the proper adjustments. I don't know how anyone does physical work in this environment.

The bait was a mixture of calf stomach and blood. Christina was busy mixing up the clotted blood with her hands. As Trude was being filmed with Ludwig, I gave Christina a hand and soon ended up looking like an extra in a horror film. Andres was motioning for me to lick my fingers. As he laughed I stuck my fingers in his mouth. He started spitting and retching, all the time trying to be quiet because the team were still filming.

Day three

Steve: We set off for another dawn raid on the warthog, but on the way there, came across Margaret, who had found a lion pride next to the road. It was decided to take the lions first because – as we have come to learn – opportunities must be seized when they occur. There were three lionesses stalking a warthog. I drove round the bushes to get a better view, but just missed the pounce. It was a gruesome death. Lions usually suffocate their prey, but warthogs have very short, thick necks. While one lioness held it down, the others tucked into its belly and leg muscles. It probably died quickly from shock, but I could choose many better ways to go. A few more adults and plenty of cubs soon joined the lionesses, making up the whole pride. It was a real feeding frenzy, with plenty of crunching sounds and disputes over the choicest pieces, resulting in snarls, growls and the occasional scuffle.

A large male buffalo appeared on the scene. It came round the bushes and was obviously quite startled by the proceedings. It stood and watched the feeding, standing about four metres from the lions, snorting in disapproval. The lions kept an eye on it but didn't stop eating. After a few minutes, the buffalo had obviously made its point, and proceeded to move away.

Did you know?

Lions are famous man killers: in 1925, two lions were held responsible for 124 human deaths and during World War II, 152 people were killed by two prides.

This was our cue to move in and dart a lion. I was handed the rifle and Margaret told me which female she wanted. I shot quickly. Yet again, I was immensely relieved when the dart struck home on target. The lions exploded in fury around the carcass. The sting of the dart was probably confused with a nip from another lion, and the female I'd hit struck out at her neighbour. This started a chain reaction among all the lions present, ending up with dinner disrupted and the lions moving away.

We waited twelve minutes and then searched for our female. We found her nicely asleep, and chased off the other lions with the vehicles. After the obligatory poke with a stick (or in this case, a gun) from the vehicle, we got out to take the samples we

needed. Andres dragged the warthog carcass away on a rope, so that the rest of the pride could return and feed without causing us any concern. There were lots of comments about him taking his pig for a walk!

Our lion was a very fit specimen. I took blood samples from a vein on the inside of the thigh, as the vein was big enough and didn't require any fur to be clipped. Ludwig monitored the anaesthetic while Margaret, Trude and I took measurements and samples galore. All in all, the lioness was asleep for an hour, which in Ludwig's opinion was too long. She was getting very twitchy towards the end and so she was revived, with a bright blindfold left over her eyes to let her wake up gently. It was half an hour before she got up, and even then she was very wobbly. She looked so comical waltzing around with a bright bandanna on her head. The pride returned to finish off the warthog and she moved towards them, which was ideal as it meant she would be safe. Ludwig waited to ensure she was OK while we returned to base to process the blood samples.

Like all laboratory work, the blood processing involved a lot of mundane tasks but we had got some interesting results. Most of the tests will be done abroad, but there are some quick 'field' kits to test for the presence of some viral diseases. Our lioness was positive for FIV, which, as with domestic cats, can remain dormant for many years without causing illness, but still remains a source of infection to other cats.

At lunch we were joined by some mongooses as they hung around the restaurant looking for scraps. They were banded mongooses and were a group being studied by two postgraduate zoologists from the University of Cambridge. Jason Gilchrist's accent easily betrayed him as a Scot, and Emily Otari is Ugandan. They were both very friendly and keen to show us their project.

Our first job was to help prepare some bait to tempt the mongooses into traps so that they could be tagged and marked. Trude's cooking skills proved to be the cause of much mirth, but Emily reassured us that the mongooses were not too fussy.

Trude: There are ten packs involved in their research but most are too wild for us to get near. One pack was much more used to humans and so are really friendly.

Steve: Emily and Jason were making humming noises as we approached. They explained that this was their way of reassuring

◄ Trude and Ludwig taking samples and measurements from the blindfolded lioness.

the mongooses that they were friends and bringing food. Someone had said that they sounded like monks moving around humming in the bushes, so they called it the 'monk call'. It isn't a noise that the mongooses make but they have learnt to associate it with food and shows we are friendly. They do have their own language, though: in fact, they never shut up. There were about thirty individuals in this pack, and they were constantly chirping and clicking away to each other. Jason told us what each sound indicated, including the alarm call, which was uttered when I whipped my foot back as one attempted to bite my toe.

Did you know?
Mongooses are very quick, and can catch and eat poisonous snakes.

Trude: Emily and Jason are trying to build up a picture of mongoose behaviour and how living near humans affects them. Apparently mongooses are cooperative breeders and all the adults, including those that aren't the parents, rear the young ones in the pack. The dominant female mates first, then the subordinate females, but all the young are born on the same day. As we walked down to the bush, we saw the males approaching the shy females.

Steve: Mongooses are so active and comical. They look very similar to ferrets – which I understand are not everybody's cup of tea – but the juveniles are so cute. They were into everything – digging, climbing, grooming and playing. It was hard keeping track of them all. Jason and Emily had put coloured collars on all the adults and ear-tagged and clipped patterns in the fur of the young. This enables them to identify specific mongooses, and record their individual behaviour. Two of the pups had lost their ear tags, so they needed trapping and tagging again.

As soon as the traps were laid down, the mongooses were clambering inside expecting to be fed. This made it a little difficult to get the ones we needed. Trude and I sat on stools about three metres away, with the trip strings in hand, ready to drop the doors. Eventually we got them – admittedly with a few extras in the traps as well. Immediately the traps were lifted, the pups started alarm-calling and the change in the pack was incredible. They all started alarm-calling and swarming around Jason, who was carrying the trap. He quickly ran back to the vehicle, where he and Trude separated the pups required before returning with the extras. When they were released they were surrounded by the others, and the whole pack turned into a huge seething mass of fur.

We drove back to the processing room to deal with the two cubs. Jason used his beard trimmer to clip the mongooses – now there's dedication for you. They are tricky to hold, but both Emily and Jason have had plenty of practice, although they've picked up battle scars on the way. The sedative combination used was identical to the one I use on ferrets, and worked very well. The mongooses were clipped and ear-tagged quickly, and left to recover in their cages to be released tomorrow. It must be like alien abduction for them – waking up in a strange place with things in their ears and shaved markings on their backs.

After a long day, we ate at the canteen in the village for the first time. The food was all local and freshly prepared. There was an awesome variety, and it was all excellent.

Day four

Steve: Getting up early is becoming totally routine now. I have been sleeping very soundly, since I have stopped taking the antimalarials. Matias spent last night at the leopard trap with Ludwig and Christina. No leopards appeared, but they witnessed a young hippo being killed by a pack of hyenas. The mother's attempts to chase them away had proved futile. I wish I had been there to observe it, but I would have been completely wrecked today if I'd stayed up.

Banded mongoose

Size: Banded mongooses look a little like ferrets but are more thickset. They are typically 25–35 cm long and weigh 1.5–2 kg.

Life span: Life expectancy is around 10 years in the wild but in captivity they have been recorded at up to 17 years old.

Distribution: They can be found from South Africa northwards to Sudan and in plentiful numbers.

Behaviour: They are very social creatures (unlike most other species of mongoose), living in groups of up to 40 individuals. However they don't share their food, preferring to eat it as soon as they find it. When threatened they will group together and writhe around each other, snapping at the aggressor to give the impression of a large multi-headed animal.

Diet: Banded mongooses are mainly insectivores but will also eat earthworms, snails, eggs, scorpions, fallen fruits and slugs.

Day six

Steve: I staggered to breakfast this morning, amazed that I was one of the first to make it. The coffee was like river mud, and failed miserably to lift me from my stupor. However, we all managed to get ourselves into the vehicles and proceeded to the hyena den armed with some bovine guts as bait. We arrived in low light, and there was little sign of activity but within ten minutes of the tape of hyenas in a feeding frenzy being played, some curious hyenas appeared from the thickets. They moved silently towards us, but never came close enough to dart. Ludwig asked me to climb on the roof to throw some bait out. The bag hummed so much that I could nearly pick out the tune! Some of the braver hyenas came nearer, and I got back inside the vehicle. Ludwig spotted one feasting on what appeared to be a horse's leg that had also been in the bait bag.

Trude: I was ready to dart and Ludwig had picked out a big female, weighing approximately seventy kilograms. My heart beat faster and faster as the time got closer. Ludwig was saying 'Not now' because we were too close. When he told me the opportunity was perfect, the hyena was staring right at me. I pulled the trigger and the dart hit spot on. I felt a rush of relief. Everyone else was happy too, as we wanted a hyena for our story.

At first the hyena looked startled and started to run away. Then she was running in circles with the other hyenas staring at her. She fell over, shaking, and we drove over to her. We did the stick test. She was fine but still trembling. She had a dog-like head, with rounded ears and her teeth were clean. Her sexual organs were amazing, as the females have secondary male characteristics with an enlarged clitoris as big as a penis, and even a small scrotal pouch. This is because female hyenas are dominant and the testosterone level in their blood is high.

Steve: After thirty-five minutes we had all the samples we needed, and I gave the reversal agent. Ludwig explained that hyenas will attack weak members in the group in order to move up the hierarchy, so it was important to reverse any anaesthetic fully. I gave one drug in the vein, which works immediately, and the other was injected into the muscles to give us a little time to retire to a safe distance. I thought the hyena was coming round quickly as it flinched when I gave it the second injection. Within a few seconds it shook its head and tried to get up. Panic ensued, with everybody trying to get into a vehicle. All the kit was left outside as the hyena got to her feet and stumbled off. We all fell about laughing, and started to pack up the gear. As we were halfway through packing up, our hyena came back to have another look at her abductors. Panic ensued for the second time. This time, however, we all knew how to do it properly. She wasn't really any threat as she was still very out of it, but it was a good reminder that one can never really relax in a job like this.

Part of the disease-monitoring scheme is to start a vaccination programme around the park. This afternoon we returned to the village where the warthog was killed and vaccinated some cats and dogs. It was really weird dealing with domestic pets in these surroundings. We caused quite a stir setting up the clinic under some trees, and soon we were surrounded by a wall of children. The dogs were all very stressed and difficult to deal with because they are mainly guard or working dogs and are not used to being handled. One dog was dragged along with a noose around its neck until it nearly passed out from exhaustion. It was bleeding at the gums from trying to chew through the rope, and was panting very hard. Ludwig told the handler, a young kid, that it was too stressed to inject today, and should be given some water and released.

Trude: We spotted a kitten in a shopping bag. It's hard to believe something so cute could be the cause of a lion dying. We were laughing a lot, and there lots of were kids flocking around. All the dogs were fine although. There is such a different attitude towards dogs here. Ludwig says they are maltreated and so they bite people.

Steve: We soon started trading animal impressions and funny noises with the kids. They shrieked in delight at each new sound, and I was then faced with about thirty attempts at reproducing it. The next half-hour was filled with blowing up latex gloves like balloons. At one point, I had one inflated on my head and was running around chasing the kids, who were squealing with laughter.

Day seven

Steve: Having missed breakfast this morning, I am looking forward to normal meals at home. The food here has been great on the whole, especially the scrambled eggs for breakfast, but I

▼ After her first darting, Trude undertakes the familiar task of taking blood samples.

am missing good tea, fresh milk and so many other things. As it happens, we could have had breakfast because the drive up to the craters where we filmed the sunrise took less time than expected, and because of the haze the sun didn't rise until after 7.30 am. The haze was very bad this morning, and Ludwig said it was the worst he had seen. We should have seen the majestic Mountains of the Moon, but any further than two kilometres became a white wash-out. The crater we could see immediately below us was very spectacular, and certainly whetted my appetite for another visit.

▲ Examining the unsuc-cessful tsetse-fly trap.

Apart from the sunrise, we had gone to this area to set tsetse fly traps. Tsetse flies are responsible for transmitting sleeping sickness. In fact, the flies are responsible for the creation of many national parks in Africa. Sleeping sickness was incurable until recently, so large areas were uninhabitable and these were designated national parks. Unfortunately the same parasite can infect livestock and wildlife, so the infection can be present without people. This means that careful monitoring of the flies needs to be carried out. If the trypanosomes that cause the illness are found, then the tsetse fly population has to be reduced. Tsetse flies have a biting mouth comparable to the great white shark's! As we drove to the spot where we were to set the trap, they invaded the vehicle. They tried biting us everywhere, and it felt like blunt needles penetrating my skin. Ludwig's driving became a little erratic as he slapped himself all over.

We stopped the vehicle and jumped out, as clearly this would be a good area in which to to catch some flies. Any onlookers would have thought we were a travelling band of Morris dancers by the way we were cavorting about trying to repel these flying nightmares. They are amazingly robust flies, and it took a great deal of violence to kill them. The usual slap, that renders the insides of your common fly visible, was nothing but a gentle pat on the back to a tsetse fly.

The traps looked like Chinese kites and were made of blue and black fabric, as flies are attracted to these colours. Once they land on the fabric, they climb up into a mesh area which they can't get out of. We left the trap and sped off, anxious to avoid these flying

◀ Trude and Steve examining the hyena that Trude has just darted – despite being her darting debut, the dart hit home first time.

carnivores. When we returned we saw that we had been thoroughly unsuccessful in catching any flies, even though there were still plenty in the vehicle. Ludwig explained that the flies are also attracted to carbon dioxide emitted by the car, possibly, in this case, more than the trap. To show the viewers at home what a tsetse fly looks like, we took some of our successful kills from the insides of the vehicles and placed them in the trap. Cheating I know, but it helps illustrate the point, and their deaths were not in vain.

We met up with Gladys Kalema, who is the chief wildlife vet for Uganda, but is only the same age as myself. She qualified as a vet from the Royal Veterinary College in London, and has a special interest in primates. She took us to see the chimpanzees that live in a river gorge not far from Queen Elizabeth Park.

Trude: I warmed to Gladys straight away. There is something about her that I can relate to. She is really chatty, and had a funny mixture of Britishness and Ugandan in her manner. She was actually a foster student where I now work. Gladys has done very well for herself and has an enormous responsibility on her shoulders. People we met on the way had insinuated that there are a lot of politics around Gladys's position. I certainly didn't care; I like Gladys, and we had a lot to talk about. Apparently she went through a lot of similar experiences at college to me, failing

Tsetse fly

Size: There are twenty-three species of tsetse fly, which range from 6–14 mm in length. They are robust flies and make a characteristic noise when flying.

Life span: Tsetse have a long life span compared to other flies, with females living for around 14 weeks and the males for around 6 weeks.

Distribution: The different species have different feeding habits, and are therefore found in different areas.

Behaviour: Tsetse flies are very important, as they can transmit parasites called trypanosomes between wildlife and domestic animals, and even to man. Trypanosomes cause sleeping sickness in humans and a disease called Nagano in domestic animals, which is usually fatal.

Diet: Tsetse feed on the widest range of host compared to other bloodsucking insects. They have been recorded as feeding off reptiles, birds, mammals and even lungfish.

her surgery exam, having to resit, and so on, so no wonder we felt like we had a lot in common.

Steve: We drove along the top of the gorge to where the rangers suggested we try descending into the gorge. The paths were well worn, steep and sandy and we half walked, half slipped down into the forest. We spotted colobus monkeys in the canopy but after a long hike, we found no chimps. It was incredible to be in the jungle, though, and we did see some hippos in the river. There was also plenty of evidence that chimps had been in the area as we found their nests and recently discarded, half-chewed fruit.

As the sun was descending it became obvious that the chimps had given us the slip, so we returned to the park where we filmed a hippo walking around the village. Andres wanted to get some photos of me and the hippo, and was encouraging me to get closer and closer. I made sure the wind was in the right direction and moved as close as I dared, making sure I knew my escape routes. A chap on a tractor passing by made chomping gestures with his hand as if to say, 'Be careful!' We got the shots and retreated from the hippo, who was munching away oblivious to the whole episode. We took his example and went for dinner.

Day eight

Steve: We said our goodbyes to Ludwig first thing this morning. He has been really patient with us, and I think he has had a good time too.

The roads were very bumpy, making it hard to read, so I slept as much as possible this morning. I was kept awake by a clinking sound from the front, though. It was a glovebox full of coffee cups from the restaurant! Dinner was a rather good packed lunch by the roadside. Andres kept all the uneaten bits in the front. I thought he would give them to the rangers, but twenty minutes down the road he stopped and dished out cake to loads

Did you know?

Tsetse females give birth to one lava at a time, and by the time it is born it weighs more than its mother.

▼ All too soon it was time to say goodbye to Ludwig, the vet at Queen Elizabeth Park.

of little kids walking home from school. I love this guy, he is such an amazingly compassionate person, given that it is very easy to become hard and cynical in this continent. He communicates so well with the people everywhere we go, regardless of race or class. For his next trick, he pulled over and gave the cups from the restaurant to an old lady walking along the road. The woman couldn't believe it, and looked at him as if he was mad.

The last part of today's journey was a climb into the hills through banana plantations. I was amazed at how the people can farm on nearly ninety-degree slopes. We eventually rounded the last bend to see a sign telling us that we had reached Bwindi Impenetrable Forest. The road ended just after the gate, proving the name of the forest to be most apt.

Bwindi is the home of many primates, with the mountain gorillas being the most famous. There are only 650 mountain gorillas left in the wild, with over half of them living here in Bwindi. Over the last three years the rangers have been habituating two gorilla groups to humans, to enable better study of them and also to allow fee-paying tourism. Very strict controls have been put in place to ensure the gorillas' welfare is upheld. Gladys explained that each group is only visited by one group of up to six tourists a day, and that they can only stay for an hour.

Trude: We arrived at Bwindi after a long drive. It was a very green place, and it looked, as the name implies, impenetrable. I have always dreamt about seeing gorillas in the wild. I have seen *Gorillas in the Mist* many times, and I was so excited to get the opportunity to see them in the flesh at last.

Steve: The gorilla trek is lined up for tomorrow, and doubles as a health check. This afternoon we had a different treat planned – a shower in the forest. There is a set of waterfalls that tourists are allowed to walk to and swim in. We enlisted the help of some porters and set off up the path. The forest was stunning. The trees were so high, and there wasn't a scrap of free space. A group of small monkeys crossed the path ahead, disturbing a whole cloud of colourful butterflies. We then turned onto a smaller path, where there were creepers and vines dangling around us and huge tree-root systems, making the steps of the tortuous path. The forest was quiet except for the chatter of the occasional bird and the creak and rustle of the trees. To think that this forest stretches over kilometres, into Congo and Rwanda is incredible. I

◄ Steve keeping a safe distance from a wandering hippo, although the hippo seems more interested in its dinner.

carried Denis's camera for a while, to give him a break because the climb was steep and occasionally hard going. The camera was remarkably light to start with but after a while it really made my shoulder ache. He must be a lot fitter than I thought to cope with this weight. When I took Dudley's kit for a bit, later on, I realized why he puffs and pants so much. It's because he is so unfit. No, only kidding – his kit is even heavier and bulkier than Denis's!

The waterfall looked like a movie set. It was perfect. Gladys and Trude weren't keen on the cold water, but I was straight in there. The temperature did cause a sharp intake of breath, but was so refreshing after the climb that I made the most of it. Behind the waterfall I found a nest with three small green eggs in it. When I told Trude, she thought it was a trick to get her wet. I eventually convinced her and she went and had a look. Try as we might, however, we couldn't get Denis to take his camera under to film it.

Chimpanzee

Size: Full adult weight is around 47–55 kg. They are the smallest of the great apes.

Life span: A chimp is considered an adult at 10 years old. Zoo animals have been recorded living up to 55 years, but it is suspected that wild chimps don't live as long due to parasites and disease.

Distribution: Chimps' preferred habitat is the rainforest but they can be found on savannahs. They are limited to small areas of central Africa and are under constant threat of habitat destruction.

Behaviour: Chimps are able to walk upright, but tend to walk on all fours with their knuckles touching the ground. Chimps are both terrestrial and arboreal (land and-tree dwelling). They live in communities of up to 100 individuals. These communities break up into smaller groups of 6–8 animals to feed, travel, rest and groom. Each group is led by an alpha male. The females migrate freely between groups. Females are sexually mature at 11–13 years old. Males are similar, but don't become sexually active until a few years later. Females tend to have a baby every 5–6 years. When the new baby is born the previously youngest child becomes independent of its mother. Mother-child bonds are very strong, and it isn't unusual for an adult to return to visit its mother.

Diet: Chimps were thought to be vegetarian, but sightings of them hunting and killing other primates and small mammals such as goats have been recorded. Quite gruesome accounts of cannibalism are not that uncommon.

Trude: I shared a tent with Gladys. We had a good chat before we went to bed, talking about boyfriends, college and becoming a vet.

Day nine

Trude: This morning we woke up and I was ready to climb. Gladys told me she took her boyfriend up to see the gorillas, to test their relationship. They trekked for eight hours and saw them for five minutes, and then trekked back. He was still keen on her after that, so I think he passed the test.

▲ Trude and Steve with Uganda's chief wildlife vet, Gladys Kalema.

Steve: Gladys needed to check on a silverback and a gorilla that she had operated on for a rectal prolapse. The silverback had been fighting with another silverback and had sustained quite a nasty injury to his back. The rangers had told Gladys that it had started to smell quite badly.

Trude: We started off at the bottom of the hill, and began the steep climb that was to last for a couple of hours. I kept on telling myself that it was going to be worth it, and also that it would be good exercise.

Steve: The climb was steep but not hard going at our pace. The porters hardly broke into a sweat, despite their hefty loads. Halfway up the climb we had a fantastic view of the Congo border, which lay along a razor-sharp ridge on the other side of the valley. We met some tourists returning, who seemed awestruck by what they'd seen. In the brief exchange we had with them, they told us how spectacular their sights of the gorillas had been. We all upped the pace, desperate to get there, and see them.

Did you know?

Chimps are fully able to make and use tools. They use sticks to pick up termites out of holes in their mounds. They have been seen using leaves to soak up water when they can't drink directly from the source. Stones are often used to break open stubborn nutshells.

Our first glimpse of the gorilla was from about a hundred metres. All we saw, though, were moving bushes and the odd black, hairy arm. We had left the path and the vegetation was very thick. We moved on slowly, with the ranger hacking a path for us to follow.

▲ Above: The impenetrable forest lives up to its name, although bits of gorilla are visible through the trees.

▶ Opposite: Steve and Trude were very fortunate to get such a close view of this group of gorillas relaxing in the forest.

Trude: We stumbled farther towards the site. The vegetation was incredibly thick, and we couldn't see where to put our feet, as everything was covered with leaves. We slid and fell and finally we got so close that we could smell and hear the gorrillas and see the flies. We almost stepped in some gorilla droppings. From now on we had to make grunting noises, and lower our heads, to make sure they knew we were friendly.

Steve: Just as we had caught up with them, there was a roaring scream and a crashing sound coming towards us through the bushes. Our tracker was being charged by one of the females. It was over before it had begun. He had stood his ground really well and she had backed off. Gladys explained that the last thing you should do is run away, even if a silverback rushes you, as they will catch and possibly kill you. If you stand your ground they will back down – usually.

The gorillas had stopped, so we climbed up the slope to get a good view of them. We came round one last corner and there they were. In all this thick vegetation they had picked a clearing under some trees to stop. We had a completely unadulterated view of them. The babies were climbing and playing and the adults were all feeding or grooming. It was a magnificent sight. Baby gorillas in the wild are perhaps the cutest thing I have seen. They fight and explore with all the same characteristics of young children. It was wonderful. At one point one of the bigger juveniles was chasing a smaller one up a small sapling. When their combined weight exceeded the strength of the tree it snapped, tumbling them both deep into the bushes. We even saw one of the adult females suckling her young. They looked so human in their facial expressions and gestures. It was amazing to see them here, in their natural environment, so relaxed.

Trude: We were lucky, catching sight of them when they were settled in a location like this. We had a perfect view of all the babies playing in the trees. A big silverback was lying on his back, with the youngsters climbing on top of him. They had big pot bellies, and fluffy coats; their hands and fingers were always grabbing something and their eyes were so human. It was like staring my ancestors in the face. They were either sleeping, dozing off or chewing on the bark from the trees they had

Gorilla

Size: Mountain gorillas are massive, with the adult males (silverbacks) reaching 2 m in height and weighing 200 kg.

Life span: The oldest gorilla in captivity was 53 years old when it died but life spans in the wild are up to 40 years.

Distribution: There are only around 650 animals left in the world, and they are all found in the volcanic peaks between the Republic of Congo, Rwanda and Uganda.

Behaviour: Gorillas live in family groups headed by a dominant silverback. The females are not related to each other, and migrate between groups. Competition over females can be quite fierce between silverbacks, even between father and sons.

Diet: Gorillas are completely vegetarian, feeding mostly on shoots and leaves more than fruit. Enough moisture is gained from their diet, so drinking is rare.

stripped. In the background we could hear the people in the villages and the dogs barking. I kept wondering who was watching who in this situation. They were certainly watching us, although it didn't seem like they were.

Steve: Gladys pointed out the gorilla that she had operated on. She explained how she had had a lot of criticism about undertaking the procedure. The rectal prolapse had been appearing for some weeks, and she was getting pressure on her to do something about it. Yet some people were saying she should leave it, as it had occurred naturally. Gladys made the decision and went ahead with the procedure. The operation is a fairly simple one in good surroundings, but must have been very difficult here in the field. Thankfully it had been a complete success, and there was still no evidence of recurrence to date, six months after the surgery.

The only downside was that the silverback who had been involved in the fight was hiding under the only cover available. We could see his arm moving around, but the only other evidence of his presence was violently audible wind. These pungent packages did little to hide the acidic stench of the rest of the gorillas. They smell of very stale sweat, the kind that makes your nose itch and your eyes sting. It was worth it though, and I'm sure they had a few things to say to each other about my personal hygiene.

Our hour was running out, and pretty soon we would have to leave. Gladys was worried that we would not get to see the silverback's wound. Then, in the last few minutes, he decided to make an appearance. Well, more of an exit, as he made to lead the group away. For a moment or two, we managed to get a reasonable look at his wound. It was a hand-sized hole on his back. It looked fairly clean and seemed to be healing well. Gladys was satisfied, so we moved away and left the gorillas in peace.

Did you know?
If a huge silverback charges at you, then it is safest to stand your ground as they will most likely stop short and put on a display of aggression. Turning and fleeing may get you killed.

The climb down was much quicker, with a short stop for lunch on the slopes. We were sweaty and tired when we reached the bottom, but couldn't wait to regale Andres and Matias with all our tales. Commendably, they listened very patiently to five versions of the same story.

Day ten

Steve: We said goodbye to Gladys and set off to Lake Mburo. The trip took about four hours. The landscape changed from forested slopes at impossible angles to valley floors heavily utilized for agriculture. The large indigenous forests are being decimated for their wood and replaced with quick-growing timber or other crops. It was disheartening to see the extent of this process but also fascinating to observe how even the steepest slopes can be farmed.

The people we are working with at the park are Joseph Okori, a Ugandan vet, and Christiane Averbeck, a German biologist. They are working with impala to determine whether there is any transmission of various diseases between them and the native cattle. There is a lot of resentment towards the impala, as they are in direct competition with the local community's cattle, and the community believes the impala are transmitting disease to their livestock. However, it may be that the cattle are transmitting disease to the wildlife. The problem is that there is no fence or barrier between the park and the surrounding land. In fact, we saw

Steve assisting with weighing the impala and taking blood samples.

cattle grazing within the park boundaries as we arrived. We also saw zebras and waterbucks on the way in and there are healthy populations of hippos, crocodiles and buffaloes. Joseph and Christiane are both very friendly and organized, even though they have to rely heavily on whoever is available to help them during the captures.

For us, one of the main attractions of this project was the novel method of capturing the animals involved. Impala are very delicate and don't respond well to darting. Also darting is very expensive and time-consuming when dealing with high numbers of individuals. The method employed here is to startle the animals with a spotlight and then grab them from behind. The hoofs are very sharp, and I made a mental note to be aware of this as it is a major contrast to the species I usually deal with. Night soon fell, and we eventually made ready to catch our impala. I was gagging to have a go as I love physical challenges. Gillian asked me to hang back on the first attempt, to get an idea of the technique before having a go myself. Christiane drove her pick-up with Trude and Joseph in the cab, and myself and the catchers on the back.

We drove along the tracks, using the spotlight from the back of the pick-up and found the first group near the camp. Their eyes reflect the light in the same way that other animals' do but they are a distinctive green colour. Once the herd was spotted, the spotlight was turned off and Christiane raced towards them with her headlights dipped. The herd immediately made for the bushes, but as we came within a metre or so of them the spotlight was turned on and they froze on the spot. We stopped in the same instant, and the guys on the back dismounted silently and half ran, half crept up behind the impala and grabbed at their legs. Most of the impala bolted a few metres on hearing their approach, but some didn't move quickly enough and were well and truly caught. I noticed that one of the guys had an impala in each hand. I grabbed one from him, carted it back towards the headlights and wrestled it to the ground. It was only a youngster and was lighter than I had imagined. I was soon helped by one of the others and we had it pinned down in no time. It took a few seconds for the dust to settle. When I looked up I realized we had three impala firmly secured to the ground. They are very slight animals with slender necks and legs.

▲ Trude, complete with head torch, examing one of the stunned impala.

Trude: Once the experts had caught the impala the other team members had to get in fast. It was the maddest thing I have ever seen. I heard someone calling for help behing me, I turned around and one of the capture team was lying on top of a massive impala. I grabbed its horns and sat across its body to keep it steady. With the impala down Joseph was able to check for parasites.

Steve: The parasites are the vehicles for diseases to be passed to other impala and, importantly, the cattle. Joseph identified the various ticks for me and we moved onto the next animal. He voiced his surprise at my lack of knowledge of African ticks, but as we really have only one important tick species in the UK, it isn't that surprising.

We then had to weigh our catch. This entailed climbing on some bathroom scales and then taking the impala in hand. They only weighed between 25 and 37 kilograms, which is roughly the weight of an adult Labrador. After ear-tagging them with large yellow tags, it only remained for us to release them.

Unfortunately the spotlight had blown during all the proceedings, leaving us high and dry. Luckily Andres had one back at camp, so we could continue. For the second capture, Denis joined us on the back of the pick-up to film the proceedings from a different angle. We set off into the darkness but the word had obviously spread, as we struggled to locate any new herds. We had been trying for about an hour when we came upon a group of three males. Christiane zoomed in and stopped within about a metre of the nearest animal. When the lads dismounted, the impala bolted for a few yards, then stopped. It was obvious they were still dazzled, and I watched one of the guys creep in and grab one of them. I rushed over and grabbed the other back leg as the impala started to struggle. Between the two of us we got it to the floor and were soon joined by the others, who grabbed the horns. Joseph got Trude to take the blood samples this time. The

Impala

Size: Impala females are smaller than the males, which can weigh up to 60 kg.

Life span: Impalas reach sexual maturity at around 3 years, and have a life span of around 14 years.

Distribution: Impalas are widespread in huge numbers in southern Africa, up to the northern limits of eastern Africa. They prefer areas of short grass for grazing and avoid tall grasslands for fear of predators.

Behaviour: April to June is the mating season, when the male impala will establish a territory to keep his females in. All young males are ejected from the herd and form into bachelor groups. After the mating season the impalas settle down into happy families and some of the young males return to the herds.

Diet: Impalas are both grazers and browsers, feeding on grasses, bushes and other vegetation. In the dry season they must drink daily, so will be found near permanent water.

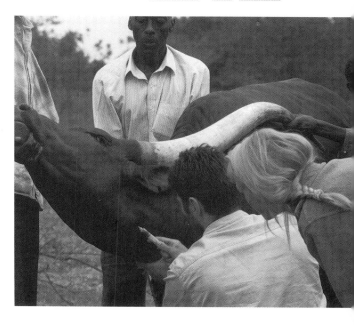

males have thicker necks, so it can be more difficult to find the jugular on them but Trude managed quite quickly. Christiane fitted the collar and was obviously very pleased with the night's work.

Day eleven

Steve: We were leaving at 7.30 am to go and see a farmer outside the park. James has a large herd of Ankole cows. The cattle are central to the people's existence and the farming of them is steeped in tradition. They have huge hollow horns that can grow to over one and a half metres. The tribe who farm them believe it was the hollow horns that saved them from drowning in a huge flood in this region. They are also directly related to wealth and status. Joseph explained that Ankole cows are kept for their milk and their beauty and are not eaten by the people, although male calves are sold to other tribes for meat. We drove some considerable distance to meet James, who has 140 cattle.

▲ Used to taking blood from the cattle for food, James is quick to help out when Steve and Trude start trying to take blood samples.

Traditionally the tribe have been nomadic, but James is planning to build a house and settle because he wants his six children to finish their education. His cattle mix freely with impala, and he understands that disease is probably spreading between the two. However, he also realizes that the wildlife brings in tourism and, more importantly for him, Joseph, who works on his animals for free as an extension of his research and as an educational tool to promote wildlife.

Did you know?

During the mating season, male impalas can get so engrossed in fights that they don't notice encroaching predators.

Trude: James is a tall, thin man with a big, white grin. He showed us around his herd, strutting like an ostrich. The Ankole were breathtakingly beautiful with their enormous snow-white horns. It's amazing that they can carry the weight of the horns so well. They are used to being handled and as we walked amongst them, no one seemed to be worried about being impaled – except me!

Michael thought it would be a good idea to show us taking blood samples from the Ankole. I struggled to raise a vein and,

▲ For James, the Ankole cattle are a way of life and part of the family.

because the calf was struggling, missed. James took over and used his traditional method. He is used to doing this, as the blood is their main source of food.

Steve: This makes up the main part of the tribe's diet, and makes great sense for nomadic people, as the cattle live off the land and they live off the cattle. James thanked us all for visiting him and his family, including the cows.

The blood samples were mainly for laboratory testing, but back at camp Joseph made a smear and he and I looked for evidence of parasites. There was evidence of East Coast fever on the smear, and Joseph told me that James had already started treatment at the last visit. Vaccinations are very expensive, and therefore the best thing James can afford to do is to treat the animals when they succumb to disease, which is why early diagnosis from Joseph is so important to him.

After a few more pick-up shots I was finished, and could relax. Trude and Christiane left to do some radio tracking, so I just read my book and enjoyed the sun. It feels so weird to have finally finished. It has been seriously hard work, but also hugely entertaining. We had a late candlelit dinner at Christiane's tent, and everybody was relieved that we could finally unwind. The other good news was that Andres had found another tent to sleep in, so I had a tent to myself. I will be fresh and bright tomorrow, without having had to listen to his snoring.

Day twelve

Trude: I can truly say that I have enjoyed every second of the time spent filming in Africa. I have learnt a lot about the people, the countries and the animals. The experience also taught me that filming is not always as glamorous as people would like to think, and that you have to be a flexible and easygoing person if you are going to enjoy things when you are under extreme environmental conditions and pressures. It's been a brilliant way to meet a lot of interesting people, who I am sure I will see again.

Steve: Travelling back to Kampala, I had time to appreciate how much I was going to miss Africa. The landscape and the people are just amazing, and I know I will return, but at the same time I am glad to be going back home. The whole trip has been one fantastic adventure after another. I have learnt so much and gained many more skills. I have also made some great friends – both human and animal. So many amazing experiences are lodged in my memory, from catching a crocodile with my bare hands to letting a cheetah lick my face. I can't wait to bore my friends and family with endless repetitions of these stories.

◀ A rare moment of relaxation during a very hectic trip.

143